MEDIEVAL MINDS

BOOKS BY THOMAS F. GRAHAM

Dynamic Psychopathology
Stars and Shadows
Medieval Minds
Profiles in Protest
Parallel Profiles
Anatomy of Aggression
Anatomy of Avarice

MEDIEVAL MINDS

MENTAL HEALTH IN THE MIDDLE AGES

THOMAS F. GRAHAM, Ph.D.

Preface by

ROBERT B. MACLEOD PH.D.

Professor of Psychology, Cornell University

London

GEORGE ALLEN & UNWIN LTD

RUSKIN HOUSE . MUSEUM STREET

PRINTED IN GREAT BRITAIN

in 11 pt. Bell Type, two pt. leaded

BY T. & A. CONSTABLE LTD.

Thence to Saint Fillan's blessed well
Whose spring can frenzied dreams dispel
And the crazed brain restore.

WALTER SCOTT

Saint Valentine, besides
To such as does his power despise
The falling sickness, sends,
And helps the man that to him cries.

THOMAS NEOGORGUS

PREFACE

Thomas Carlyle said, 'History is the essence of innumerable biographies'. This may not be a prescription for all histories of science, but for the historian who would tell the story of man's quest for self-understanding, the advice is sound. With a certain amount of ingenuity it is possible to present the history of mathematics and the physical sciences as an orderly progression from ignorance to wisdom, each new set of discoveries serving as supports for the still newer discoveries of a succeeding generation.

If we schematize the history of physical theory since the seventeenth century, we can see how the achievements of the nuclear age would have been impossible without an earlier mastery of simpler and cruder principles of electrical transmission and mechanical causation. Thus in a limited sense we may say that the data with which the scientist works are the accomplishments of his predecessors. But only in a very limited sense. No really great scientist has been a mere builder on the accomplishments of others. Isaac Newton could draw both facts and insights from Galileo, and Hermann Helmholtz could extend the work of Johannes Müller, but it was the genius of each to see familiar facts in a new and larger context. The men who have led the forward march of science have been, more often than not, challengers of tradition rather than conformists. And here is where the human side of history becomes important. Behind the apparently orderly progression from discovery to discovery is the story of living human beings whose restless curiosity has led them to re-examine old assumptions and to take a fresh look at familiar facts. It may be that in our study of the history of science we can learn as much from the story of the scientist as we can from a catalogue of his accomplishments.

This is true of the history of the science of man. To try to write the history of psychology as a succession of forward steps would be a misguided effort. Psychologists have not in orderly fashion been building insight upon insight. Similar to the newborn child, whose parents' skills are not inherited, the psychologist of each generation must grapple afresh with the problems of living and through his own experience arrive at insights which for him are meaningful. In a negative sense, perhaps, there has been progress in psychological thinking. Some of the more crippling superstitions of the past have been overome, and some of the more egregious errors of our forefathers can be quickly recognized and dismissed. This is no guarantee, however, that thinking can now proceed without constraint or bias. The implicit assumptions of today may tomorrow be scorned as twentieth-century superstitions, and yesterday's psychological insights may within their own framework be as profound as those of today.

If we set aside the notion that the history of psychology must reveal progress from ignorance to wisdom, why then should we continue to study history? There are many answers, the most telling of which lies in the uniqueness of psychology's subject matter. The data of psychology, unlike those of the physical sciences, are in essence the same for twentieth-century man as they were for Aristotle. They are the phenomena of what used to be called 'the human mind', and the first steps towards a psychology are taken when one begins to be curious about human experience. At different times and in different places people have observed, described and conceptualized experience in different ways. The attempt to recreate the human problem as it has been seen through other eyes is often a humbling experience, revealing the poverty of our own observation and the barrenness of our theorizing. This is not to suggest that the psychologist of today should discard his theoretical models and to return to Aristotle; in fact he will gain little from Aristotle if he is not himself in active search of a theory. He will be a better psychologist, however, if he realizes that the passage of centuries does not necessarily diminish the value of a psychological insight.

Thomas F. Graham has been exploring the highways and the byways of the Mental Health movement for some years. He has searched and researched in an area that is too often neglected by the academic historians of psychology. It is an area that contains a fascinating story, for many of the subjects are complex and puzzling people. Quite apart from its human appeal, however, it is essential to an understanding of man's conceptions of

8

PREFACE

himself and of his relations to the world around him. In this little book, the author covers the period from the second century to the budding of the scientific Renaissance, a period during which man's conception of the good and healthy life was part and parcel of his theology. We think of the medieval ideas as primitive in comparison with those of the Greeks or of ourselves. Yet anxiety and fear, guilt and hatred are the same, even though clothed in varied guises, and the ways in which people in different cultural settings have coped with them are illuminating as well as interesting. Dr Graham gives us glimpses into the recesses of scores of medieval minds, glimpses which invite us to further study and reflection.

ROBERT B. MACLEOD, Ph.D.
Professor of Psychology
Cornell University

ACKNOWLEDGMENT

To cite references, I am indebted to numerous authors and publishers. Specific acknowledgment is made in the text and/or bibliography for all quotations and verses. For assistance in locating historic volumes, I thank the librarians and staffs of the National Library of Medicine, Harvard College Library, the Bibliothèque de L'Académie Nationale de Médecine, Paris, the Canton Public Library and the Massillon Public Library. Sincere thanks is also accorded to Princeton University, the Library of Congress, University of Basel and those individuals listed for illustrations.

Massillon, Ohio   THOMAS F. GRAHAM
January, 1966

CONTENTS

CONTENTS

ILLUSTRATIONS

INTRODUCTION

As the enigmatic figures of antiquity fade into the remote passageways of our minds, we awaken to the muffled sounds of medieval life. Though we now have some notion of what caused ancient men to despair, what encouraged them to hope, what stirred them to dream and what motivated them to think about their behaviour, we still hear of simple and primitive explanations. Bizarre beliefs relate mental disorders to evil spirits. Treatments consist of peregrinations in the occult. Relentless and grim efforts try to lure the demons out of the possessed. Active measures such as beatings, trepanations and venesections are administered to drive devils (who supposedly assumed living forms) out of their tormented victims. Attempting to maintain adjustment, many of the people wear amulets, talismans and the remains of animals or of men.

Opening the early Christian centuries, we may stagger with Montanus, Origen and Simeon; regain balance with Basil and Julian; interpret the mental health views of Augustine; translate medical works with Aurelianus; smile at the anecdotes of Alexander of Tralles and reaffirm the past in the person of Paul of Aegina. Then we may discard the charms of the ancients and replace them with the emblems, images and relics of the mounting number of holy men and women who had been or were being canonized as saints.

These were static and secure centuries; the centuries of stability and of surety; of fixed ideas and of settled issues. These were the centuries of certainty about what was good or evil; what was right or wrong; what was true or false. These were the centuries of set standards when none had to doubt; none had to inquire; none had to wonder. They knew! They knew that there was nothing to change. They knew that the essentials were in place; they knew that all things were clear.

The dogmatic fixity of these centuries went on until shaken up by hordes of invading Arabs who stormed out of the Middle East, the land where the sun and man were born. They were to be known as 'barbarians', the same 'barbarian' people of Cordova who bathed in luxury at a time that the 'cultured' natives of Oxford considered washing to be a dangerous practice.

Before and after these developments took shape, we may examine the multiphasic personality traits of Mohammed; list psychiatric syndromes meticulously with Unhammad; watch Rhazes rise from a roustabout matinée idol to a great clinician; travel the festive circuit with the rollicking and the philandering Avicenna; open a vista of scientific inquiry with Averroes and tour the beautifully appointed Mansuri Hospital. And we may introduce the forerunners of projective doll play, therapeutic puppetry and modern psychodrama.

Then we enter the twelfth century, a century that launched an age of crises and of conflicts. It was an ambivalent age, indeed, for mental health. It was an age of the irrational Michael Psellus who revived the ancient lore of demonology and of the forensic-minded Irnerius who opposed these views. It was an age of Abélard and Héloïse who carried on an illicit affair, and of Canon Fulbert who acted to destroy their romance. It was an age of the priestly Bartholomew who did wonders for the insane and of the sadistic psychopaths who operated Bedlam. It was an age of the scientific Roger Bacon and the mystic Duns Scotus; the logic-chopping Thomas Aquinas and the bloodletting Arnold of Villanova.

It was an age that correlated the morbid words of the authors who published the *Malleus Maleficarum* and the eerie works of the artists who splashed on canvas the fantastic beliefs of that day. It was an age of the stirring Crusades and the promising Renaissance; of the terrible Inquisition and the fulminating Reformation.

To ignore the fact that mental health had a vital part in all of these events and especially in the highly explosive Reformation is as unreal as to deny that Martin Luther ever lived. It seems that man must pass through some anxious and some tantalizing years, from time to time, if he is to reach maturity.

INTRODUCTION

Such were the Reformation years—years when religious controversy drained human energies which would have, otherwise, flowed into creative work. Similarities were overlooked; differences were accented; polemic debates obscured the real reforms and chauvinistic belligerence became the order of the day. The reformers held a persistent disbelief in the intentions of the Catholic Church; and not to be outdone, even in suspiciousness, the churchmen felt equally dubious about the reformers.

Soon affairs were strained to the breaking point and any hope of reconciliation looked tormented. Encouraged by the state, the dissenters launched all-out efforts to create a new kind of a world—a world which they sincerely believed would meet human needs honestly and effectively, a world which would make Christ accessible directly to man. Thus, the Reformation opened as a movement of faith; but sadly closed as a movement of law—of law more diligent and more exact in persecution of heretics than the Church it sought to reform.

With each convert, the reformers lost sight of their initial aims and became inordinately obsessed with perpetuating the tremendous power that had fallen to them. Men of action, like Martin Luther and John Calvin, raged against the old order in Rome and endeavoured to make proposals conform to their own concepts of righteousness. They spared no effort to glorify their new faiths as the ultimate stages in man's centuries-long search for the truth. Since the reformers could not offer anything in the present, they offered 'salvation and happiness in the next life', and instilled lasting qualities into their movements. Unfortunately, the Reformation retained its active phase only long enough to ignite destructive and violent forces. Johann Goethe believed that the disorder would have been prevented if the religious conflicts had been referred to clear-thinking men instead of to hot-headed zealots.

It was also an age of those mental health revolutionaries, the battling Heinrich Agrippa, the bombastic Philippus Paracelsus and the methodical Johann Weyer who tried heroically to lift man off the steaming floor of hell. It was an age of François Rabelais who expounded mental health ideas in fiction; of Jean Fernel in medicine; of Jean Bodin in law.

It was an age that bridged ancient with modern, ignorance with knowledge, superstition with science. It was also an age of men who passionately sought to integrate the darkness of the past with the light of the future by reducing contemporary resistance as time seemed to run out on them. These were the men whose minds and lives spanned almost a millennium in the history of mental health.

CHAPTER ONE

MONTANUS TO DYMPNA

Since Christian doctrine was not fully matured in the post-Galenic era, many thinkers returned to Plato's profound concept, a system which assumed that ideas existed independently beyond the physical realm. That is, ideation meant an absolutely pure condensation of abstraction, and the external environment represented only imperfect partial mirrors of these ideas. This attitude became of utmost significance to theoretical psychology and eventually to applied mental health, because under such conditions the Medieval Ages rode in on a wave of Platonic subjectivity and remained so until the thirteenth century when Aristotelian objectivity was revived.

Some of the most revealing indices of these times emanated from the works of Akiba and Philo. The former, Akiba, directed a rabbinical school in Jaffa where he expounded cabala—a kind of theosophy which interpreted the Scriptures in a mystical manner. And Philo, 'the Jewish Plato', tried to integrate the philosophy of religion, as taken from the Greeks, with the tenets of the Pentateuch. Both men turned the calendar back centuries by their claim that countless spirits inhabited the world and were responsible for mental disorders.

This age also saw the growth of Gnosticism—a system preaching salvation through knowledge where esoteric sects dated their own era and borrowed formulas of various early religions and blended them with Christianity to define matter as inimical to spirit. Add to this wave of occultism the intense asceticism of the churches and we have an almost complete breakaway from the clinical atmosphere of the days of Clarissimus Galen.

Accepting evil spirits as a reality, both Judaism and Christianity tried to suppress occultism by forbidding anyone to deal in such practices. They endowed man with a free will; they assumed that a perversion of behaviour often resulted from voluntary submission to the forces of the devil; and they hoped that coercion and intimidation, reason and experience meant the end of diabolism. But the ancient superstitions lived on—revitalized by another name. Even modern materialism failed to stamp out the old ideas—renewed in the nineteenth century as spiritism and more recently as parapsychology.

MINDS OF MYSTICS

Not aware of mental illness as such, the theologians of the early Christian era also ascribed bizarre reactions to divine intervention. Anything purely human was depreciated. When psychotics manifested religious delusions, the puzzling question that arose was were they inspired by God or possessed by Satan? One such case took place in the second century when a Phrygian convert, called Montanus, announced with frenzied ecstasy: 'I am the Lord God Who dwell in Man'. With two women companions, Maximilla and Prisca, he called the people together, ordered rigid fasting and observances in preparation for the immediate second coming of Christ. The proclamations of these three mentally sick people won favour with many, including the eloquent African lawyer Quintus Tertullian.

From a dynamic point of view, Montanus seemed compelled to transcend himself, to go beyond the needs of his nature. He had what may be called a need for sublimity or ecstasy. Through such transcendence, he tried to realize his full being, by eagerly seeking ecstatic experiences that had a special meaning for him. In this ecstasy all the bonds that confined Montanus were removed, and there was a soaring that unified his inner and outer identities. Once these were exemplified, the design was set for the 'possible' return of Christ—a longing for what might be as compared to what was.

It may be that Montanus, like any lonely person, sensed the discrepancy between what was and what might be for his own state of being-in-the-world. The larger the index, the greater the feeling of loneliness for him. But in a psychotic ecstasy, loneliness was not a problem; for he permitted his inner identity to flower in a way known only to the primary process: what *was* was what might be.[1]

Montanus' reaction, quite clearly, provided an insight into the cultural picture of that period whether in Phrygia or Rome. Because of the nature of mental illness, it bore an intimate relationship to the culture in which it existed. It mattered little to anyone if the approach to the problem was realistic or otherwise; and the more man looked into himself, the more anxiously involved he became in the very thing he wanted to understand and manage—his mind. When nature refused to unlock the secrets of his mind, medieval man turned frequently to oriental cults with their orgiastic rituals and drunken revelries to demonstrate the most unusual mastery over his body whether it was beaten, burned, castrated or crucified. The fact that he felt no pain while receiving such brutal punishment convinced him, more than ever, of the 'truth' of his new-found faith.

Origen, one of the bitterest foes of science, represented a classical example of an extreme view even for those days. His writings stamped him as an important witness of the uncompromising attitudes that pervaded this early era—an era in which injury of limb, sickness of body and derangement of mind were correlated positively with demons. Converted to Christianity at eighteen, Origen soon acted out his ecstatic faith by gelding himself to destroy any carnal drive that would again lead him to sin.

Perhaps Origen made a liberal interpretation of Matthew 12 : 12: 'For there are eunuchs who have been made so from birth, and there are eunuchs who have been made eunuchs by men, and there are eunuchs who have made themselves eunuchs for the sake of the kingdom of heaven. He who is able to receive this, let him receive it.' Then too, Origen's grief and remorse in his 'sad and doleful lamentations after his fall, in the days of

Severus', may have compelled him to take the only alternative left to him of having his hitherto undefiled body polluted by miscreants.

Simeon Stylites, a contemporary of Augustine, was another mystic who illustrated the rise of a strange form of asceticism which added to the theological chaos in this age of 'systematic insanity'. As a youth, Simeon sought to impress upon the 'sinful' the necessity for penance when he crouched at the gate of a monastery for several days without food to gain admittance. Later counselled out of the religious order as being unsuitable, he continued his extreme austerity, mortified himself by long periods of fasting, tortured his body by burying it up to the neck or by standing upright until his limbs would no longer sustain him. Seeking solitude, he withdrew from the community and confined himself in a tiny hut.

But when pilgrims clamoured for him, he made himself available by moving to a platform that had been erected on the ruins of a building where he stayed many years and acquired the name pillar-saint from the Greek *stylos*. His first abode was about nine feet high, only to be replaced by others; the last one towered more than fifty feet above the ground. From this lofty perch, Simeon preached and performed various self-punitive exercises.

Could it be that the stress faced by Simeon acted as a stimulus to self-growth or as a defence against total ego disorganization? It seems impressively clear that his subliminal deviations, his *formes frustes* of a psychosis, were related to a morbid need to relieve guilt. One chronicler tells us that Simeon lived with a rope tightly embedded in his waist and since he regarded bathing a vice that aggrandized the flesh, 'a horrible stench, intolerable to the bystanders, exhaled from his body, and worms dropped from him whenever he moved, and they filled his bed'.[2]

Basil the Great, a prominent bishop and saint of the same fourth century, wrote one of the brighter chapters in the annals of mental health. He built a town hospital with a special unit for the insane. The charge was often made that Christians like Basil were unfortunately influenced by the scriptural reference to evil spirits and blamed all disorders on demonical possession. As a consequence, the insane were believed to be abused and neglected. The reverse would have been more true, for Basil and a group of Christians, however small, definitely held a sympathetic understanding of the mentally ill. Julian, a pagan and classmate of Basil, frankly stated that his own intention was to rival the philanthropic work of the Christians who cared for the pagans as well as those of their faith.[3]

AUGUSTINE OF HIPPO

Augustine of Hippo was born in Tagaste, Africa, when Basil was still in his twenties. Son of Patricius, a pagan, and Monica, a Christian, Augustine grew up to be a robust young man with a lustful appetite before he developed a *superego* and became sorely troubled with feelings of guilt—guilt so intense that it could not be stilled by any amount of learning or rationalizing. Faced with an enigma of existence, he then tried and dropped Manichaeism —a mystical theology that depicted Satan as co-eternal with God. Next he turned to Christianity after being roused by the history of St Anthony and the conversion of two of his own friends. The crisis came when in a depressive mood Augustine ran to the garden weeping: 'Thou, O Lord, how long? how long, Lord, wilt Thou be angry forever? Remember not our former iniquities, for I felt that I was held by them. I sent up these sorrowful words: How long, how long, "tomorrow, and tomorrow?" Why not now? why not is there this hour an end to my uncleaness?'

While in this bitter, contrite state of mind, he heard the voice of a child chanting: 'Take up and read; Take up and read'. This may have been a kind of eidetic imagery recalled from his past, but Augustine, believing that the voice was a command from heaven, obeyed it eagerly, ran inside and opened the Scripture to see: 'Not in rioting and drunkness, not in chambering and wantonness, not in strife and envying; but put ye on the Lord Jesus Christ, and make not provision for the flesh, in concupiscence'. 'No further would I read; nor needed I: for instantly at the end of this sentence, by a light as it were of serenity infused into my heart, all the darkness of doubt vanished away.'[4] Augustine was about twenty at the time. Several years later he left for Italy to teach rhetoric, where he subsequently met Ambrose who baptized him.

All of this had little bearing upon mental health, as such, until Augustine began to debate and write about the perplexing problems of his day. It was then that he came forth with specious quasi-explanations which reinforced the age-old view that man inherited a will to wickedness rather than one to goodness. In a most heated controversy, Augustine gained a tainted victory over Pelagius, who had argued that man had a freedom of will to do both good and evil. Pelagius was an English monk who had denied original sin and rejected the Christian concept of grace.

Whether Augustine or Pelagius appeared more nearly right was a moot question. Augustine's train of thought, linked to the Latins, emphasized guilt rather than its punishment; whereas Pelagius, drawing principles mainly from the Greeks, placed greater stress on the punishment. What was important was that such semantic differences added to the confusion, prolonged the indecision and divided men to a point that darkness engulfed the entire field of mental health for hundreds of years. Even today the darkness remains. Who is to blame? Some say Adam. Some say Augustine. Does it really matter? Consider these remarks[5]:

'That the whole human race has been condemned in its first origin, this life itself, if life it is to be called, bears witness by the host of cruel ills with which it is filled. Is not this proved by the profound and dreadful ignorance which produces all the errors that enfold the children of Adam, and from which no man can be delivered without toil, pain, and fear? Is it not proved by his love of so many vain and hurtful things, which produces gnawing cares, disquiet, griefs, fears, wild joys, quarrels, law-suits, wars, treasons, angers, hatreds, deceit, flattery, fraud, theft, robbery, perfidy, pride, ambition, envy, murders, parricides, cruelty, ferocity, wickedness, luxury, insolence, impudence, shameless-

ness, fornications, adulteries, incests, and the numberless un-
cleannesses and unnatural acts of both sexes, which it is shameful
so much as to mention; sacrileges, heresies, blasphemies, per-
juries, oppression of the innocent, calumnies, plots, falsehoods,
false witnessings, unrighteous judgments, violent deeds,
plunderings, and whatever similar wickedness has found its way
into the lives of men, though it cannot find its way into the
conception of pure minds? These are indeed the crimes of wicked
men, yet they spring from that root of error and misplaced love
which is born with every son of Adam. For who is there that has
not observed with what profound ignorance, manifesting itself
even in infancy, and with what superfluity of foolish desires,
beginning to appear in boyhood, man comes into this life, so that,
were he left to live as he pleased, and to do whatever he pleased,
he would plunge into all, or certainly into many, of those crimes
and iniquities which I mentioned, and could not mention?'

Thus in *The City of God*, a detailed exegesis of the Catholic
Church, Augustine formulated traditional principles of human
behaviour. His works, reflecting a philosophy of that day and
resurrecting the ghost of Platonism, were sadly applied to mental health. While he may have been unaware of it, Augustine's
idealism failed to define accurately the relationship of theology,
philosophy and psychology, and like Plato he considered all
processes psychical. The physical was not important since the
body was a mystery; and for centuries thereafter, revelation and
reasoning lived in coexistence where Christian concepts of
psychology wore a Platonic cape cut and tailored for the needs of
medieval asceticism.

In his psychology, Augustine maintained that the soul and
body formed one substance—man. The soul gave being and
species to the body. It acted on the body. The body, however,
had no independent power of acting on the soul. Whatever
power the body possessed was conferred on it by the soul.
Between the soul and the body was interposed a subtle element
that shared at the same time of the spiritual nature of the soul
and of the material nature of the body. This element, Augustine

added, was analogous to light and air. Its function was to mediate between the soul and the organs of the body, and to unite, in some mysterious way, soul and body in one substance.

When Augustine lived, his keen mind explored the depths of the human soul, exposed its doubts and revealed its uncertainties. After he died, his manifold studies provided weapons for future critics and defenders of his views. H. A. Overstreet, with the authoritative air of a modern scientist and the pen of a philosopher-theologian, blamed Augustine for much of man's trouble[6]:

'In fact, Augustine's position was so flagrantly a projection upon the whole human race of his own uncontrollable lusts that a modern psychologist would have thrown out his contentions as untrustworthy and misconceived. Thus the greatest question at issue in our human life—whether we start with powers that enable us fairly well to work out our destiny; or whether, by a mysterious curse, we are defeated at the outset and must appeal to a higher Power to help us out—was settled without the slightest attempt to search for relevant factual evidence. It was settled by sacred writings, by theological disputations, and by theological politics. We might almost say that the curse which, through all subsequent centuries, has rested upon man came, not from Adam, but from Augustine. To a peculiar degree, it was Augustine who denied to our species the healthy blessing of self-respect.'

Fulton J. Sheen, on the other hand, with the convincing word of an articulate bishop and the pen of a theologian-philosopher, saw Augustine in an entirely different light. This is what he wrote in the 'Introduction' to the *Confessions:*

'He is the most modern of writers first of all because he lived in a period very much like the twentieth century, with the fall of Rome corresponding to the decline of Western civilisation, when human hearts sick with the odours of the dying lily of paganism were frustrated and unhappy. There is no difference in the way chemical or physical laws operate now than in the fourth century, and there is no difference in the way moral and psychological laws work either. Loss of the meaning of life throughout all centuries has always produced two effects: one social and the other individual. The social effect is political anarchy or the spirit of revolution which takes vengeance on society for not supplying the goal of life. The individual effect is carnal licence which seeks to make the intensity of an erotic experience compensate for the loss of purpose. St Augustine wrote of the first in his *City of God* and of the second in his *Confessions*, thus covering both the sociology and the psychology of a culture in disintegration. In the first, he showed that just as there is potential life under the shell of an egg, but that life cannot assert itself until the shell is broken, so the incipient Christian life, which was confined under the shell of paganism, could not become the vitalizing principle of a new society until the shell was crushed by the barbarian who later on came to be an integral part of that new Christian life. Long before the world heard of Heidegger and Kierkegaard, who wrote philosophy born out of catastrophe, St Augustine, with greater crystalline purity and with more diamond-like brilliance, wrote in his *Confessions* the poignant inner experience of the soul catastrophe in a catastrophic world.

'Not only does he reveal himself as the last of the great metaphysics of the Patristic period, but also the first of all modern psychologists. It is precisely at this point that the *Confessions* make their great appeal. Modern man lives in a psychological cell where he has locked himself consciously, but is now trying to find some way of getting out, particularly through the cellar door of the unconscious. Man once lived in a three-dimensional universe with heaven above, hell below and the earth in the middle, as a place of pilgrimage or a moment of novitiate where the soul could say "aye" or "nay" to one of its eternal destinies. In this hierarchy of creation, each temporal act became fraught with eternal significance. But with the gradual apostasy from Divinity, the two eternities were rejected and man conceived himself as living on a horizontal plane of materialism, where his chief aim was either to make money or to have a good time, and both if possible. But with depressions, wars and increasing insecurities, this material surface began to shrink up and up, until finally man got locked inside of his own ego. Just as philosophers, like Marx, tried to find a way out of economic egotism by abandoning conscience, morality, responsibility and exploring the underground of the de-personalized and de-conscienced masses, where man was said to be determined by economic forces, so psychologists thought that they could find a way out by plunging below reason into the deep, cavernous, libidinous, primitive, carnal urges of the unconscious. What the masses were to Marx, that the *id* was to certain erotic psychologists. Both systems proved unsuccessful in giving man peace of soul, for when human reason is not crossed from above by faith, it is crossed from below by the irrational and the insane. *The City of God* gives the proper answer to the first error by revealing the moral basis of history, and the *Confessions* the cure for the second by proclaiming the sovereignty of love.'

While both Overstreet and Sheen were aware of the psychological dark age in which Augustine lived, they none the less focused their critique on Augustine the man. These were anxious and paradoxical times as Christian dogma tried to find itself; man began to lose himself in spite of the fact that ancient theology had endowed him with an absolutely free will. All men of that day were condemned to a state of emotional dependency, as it were, on a Supreme Being. Whether mentally healthy or not, man seemed much like a dependent child—unable to work out his own adjustment—but, in reality, his dependency was upon the age in which he lived, an age that had not matured enough to define accurately the relations between theology and philosophy, theology and psychology, and philosophy and psychology. These tasks, reserved for master minds of future centuries, remain enigmatic to the present day. The real test will come, of course, when poetically expressed opinions and eloquently phrased theories must be implemented by 'down-to-earth' decisions.

The patron of brewers, printers and theologians, Augustine held noteworthy ideas about suicide, only to confuse the role of mental disorders in such cases. Reference is made here to his comments on suicide, because suicide is an index, however rough, of mental disorders in a population at any given time. Augustine based his denial of self-destruction on a number of points some of which were illustrated in Book I of *The City of God*:

'Of suicide committed through fear of punishment or dishonour. And consequently, even if some of these virgins killed themselves to avoid such disgrace, who that has any human feeling would refuse to forgive them? . . . For it is not lawful to take the law into our own hands, and slay even a guilty person, whose death no public sentence has warranted, then certainly he who kills himself is a homicide, and so much the guiltier of his own death, as he was more innocent of that offence for which he doomed himself to die.' Committing suicide in order to avoid committing a sin was considered to be a greater sin, because it was then impossible to repent.

'Of Lucretia, who put an end to her life because of the outrage done her. . . . This crime was committeed by Lucretia; that Lucretia so celebrated and lauded slew the innocent, chaste, outraged Lucretia. Pronounce sentence. But if you cannot, because there does not compeer any one whom you can punish, why do you extol with such unmeasured laudation her who slew an innocent and chaste woman? Assuredly you will find it impossible to defend her before the judges of the realms below, if they be such as your poets (Virgil in *Aeneid*) are fond of representing them; for she is among those

> Who guiltless sent themselves to doom,
> And all for loathing of the day,
> In madness threw their lives away.

'That Christians have no authority for committing suicide in any circumstances whatever. . . . Nay, the law, rightly interpreted, even prohibits suicide, where it says, "Thou shalt not kill". This is proved specially by the omission of the words "thy neighbour", which are inserted when false witness is forbidden: "Thou shalt not bear false witness against thy neighbour". Nor yet should any one on this account suppose he has not broken this commandment if he has borne false witness only against himself. For the love of our neighbour is regulated by the love of ourselves, as it is written, "Thou shalt love thy neighbour as thyself" . . . "Thou shalt not kill", to pull a flower? Are we thus insanely to countenance the foolish error of the Manichaeans? Putting aside, then, these ravings, if, when we say, Thou shalt not kill, we do not understand this of plants, since they have no sensation, nor of the irrational animals that fly, swim, walk, or creep, since they are dissociated from us by their want of reason, and there are therefore by the just appointment of the Creator subjected to us to kill or keep alive for our own uses; if so, then it remains that we understand that commandment simply of man. The commandment is, "Thou shalt not kill man"; therefore neither another nor yourself, for he who kills himself still kills nothing else than man.'

Aside from plants and animals, Augustine allowed exceptions in which men may be killed without incurring the guilt of murder. These exceptions he justified by a general law that would 'put to death wicked men', or by a special commission as in war or by a divine command: 'Abraham indeed was not merely deemed guiltless of cruelty, but was even applauded for his piety, because he was ready to slay his son in obedience to God, not to his own passion . . . that Jephthah killed his daughter, because she met him when he had vowed that he would sacrifice to God whatever first met him as he returned victorious from battle. Samson, too, who drew down the house on himself and his foes together, is justified only on the ground that the Spirit who wrought wonders by him had given him secret instructions to do this. . . .'

One must wonder in this sixth decade of the twentieth century how long Augustine's pious-sounding rationalizations influenced man. More than a hundred years after Augustine, the Council of Braga (563) condemned suicide as a crime and deprived the individual taking his own life of a Christian burial. The Council of Toledo (693) imposed the penalty of excommunication for anyone attempting to do away with himself. It also decried suicide as a means toward martyrdom. Finally, in the twelfth century the psychotic who tried suicide and failed was exempted from penalty by the *Decretum de Gratian* which then qualified the Canon with the term *voluntarie*, wherein a person could be punished only if he committed any illegal act voluntarily.

MENTAL THERAPISTS

Almost fifty years after the death of Augustine, Rome fell and Byzantine assumed a leading position not only in the then known world but also in the world of mental health. The new empire produced several figures who approached clinical problems with some degree of sophistication; they were Caelius Aurelianus, Alexander of Tralles and Paul of Aegina.

Caelius Aurelianus, a physician from Rome and Carthage, lived sometime between the first and fifth centuries. While little has been discovered about his personal life, he is best remembered for having rendered the medical works of Soranus and Ephesus into a barbarous albeit readable Latin. Caelius commands admiration for preserving the enlightened views of Soranus, a man who went to infinite details to comfort the hyperactive patient rather than to control him: [7]

He would not tolerate any employee who whipped a patient to make him obey, which he spoke of as applied to the face and head, so as to cause swellings and sores. He recognized the mental distress that an unfortunate patient would suffer on regaining consciousness. He placed the acutely disturbed in a room moderately light and warm, and removed everything which might excite him. He recommended a firm bed, probably fixed to the floor, and situated so that the patient would not be distracted by seeing others enter the room. Straw, soft and well beaten, but not broken, served as a mattress. Should the patient try to injure himself he was padded on the back and chest with soft wool.

His rules for the attendants were 'minute and praiseworthy' and compared favourably with the corresponding regulations in the nineteenth-century *Handbook* prepared by the Scottish Medico-Psychological Association. Attendants were alerted not to confirm the patient's delusions, and so deepen his malady: they were taught not to exasperate him by needless opposition, and instead to endeavour to correct his delusions, 'at one time by indulging condescension, and at another by insinuations'.

Warm sponges were applied over the patient's eyelids to relax them, and to exert a beneficial influence on the membranes of the brain. Restlessness and sleeplessness were treated by carrying the patient about on a litter. During convalescence, the patient went to dramas and plays and witnessed scenes of a solemn or tragic character supposedly to lessen his excitement.

Caelius denounced the meagre diet which Celsus had extolled, and asserted that induced hunger was more likely to cause than to cure madness. He objected strongly against putting a patient in chains. He opposed the common practice of making a patient intoxicated. He would not approve of aloes, hellebore and venesection because these measures sapped the energy of the patient. He favoured emollient and astringent applications to soothe and invigorate the patient. *'Vinum vel amor'*, often prescribed by Asclepiades, was reprobated by Caelius.

The humanistic and understanding tone of Soranus, echoed by Caelius, sounded a new note in early psychotherapy. Both men believed, for example, that farmers should be engaged in conversation about the soil, sailors about the sea and illiterates about elementary topics—in a sense—anticipating modern remotivation therapy. And for the intellectuals, disputations of philosophers were highly regarded, for mental symptoms could be often dispelled in this way by challenging the *ego* ideal of the patient.

Alexander of Tralles, Greek physician who visited Africa, Gaul and Spain, probably also practised medicine and taught in Rome. Notable for his *Twelve Books on Medicine*, he enjoyed a fine contemporary reputation.

Aware of the influence of mind on body, Alexander gave a plausible description of mental disorders, but when it came to treatment, he paradoxically failed to select remedies judiciously, and instead prescribed amulets, bleeding, aloes and the like. In contrast to Caelius, who emphasized the clinical humanitarian approach, Alexander tried some cute, clever tricks such as making a patient wear a leaden hat to 'cure' him of the nihilistic delusion that he had no head.

Another amusing tale with several twists concerned a woman who believed that she had swallowed a snake which remained in her stomach and caused her acute pain when she did not eat large amounts of food. Trallianus, as he was also called, gave her an emetic and then slipped a snake into the basin she used for vomiting. The ruse supposedly resulted in a complete recovery. But other variants of the same story reported a temporary cure, for the patient was more sure than not that while in her stomach the snake gave birth to young.

Paul of Aegina was the last famous Greek doctor to live in Rome, and although he had only a routine interest in insanity he still managed to compile much that had been written on the subject by the ancients. He reiterated the need for treating the mentally ill in a kind and gentle manner. More specifically, he advised that these patients be put in a quiet institution where they could receive hydrotherapy and have opportunities for recreation to divert their minds to more wholesome channels.

Unlike Alexander of Tralles, a transitional figure who challenged the authority of the past, Paul of Aegina simply re-affirmed what had been written by the ancients. A humble, un-assuming man, he claimed nothing for himself; and he un-equivocally accepted the methods of those before him. In a word, he would have fitted in nicely with the logic-chopping scholastics of the thirteenth century; but he lived at a time when the golden-domed city of Byzantium, bulwark of Christianity, was besieged by Arabs, Tartars and Ottomans.[8]

Confined to their beset city, the Byzantine doctors—Alex-ander of Tralles and Paul of Aegina—regressed more than a millennium far into the past until they reached the sources of classical knowledge. The mental health they studied and practised was much like the medical compilations of Oribasius and Aetios in that it symbolized a flight into time. The works of the Byzantine artists also symbolized this escape from the surrounded city by falling back into antiquity with time-consuming stained-glass work, enamels, miniatures and illuminated manuscripts.

SAINTS AND SANITY

Not all allusions to mental health in these early centuries were found in the minds of mystics, the theories of theologians or the practice of doctors. As the Middle Ages gained momentum, and the Catholic Church grew powerful, another factor, the influence of saints, moved on to the mental health stage. Medieval Christians then believed that a saint had the power to cure or even inflict a disorder. At times, the affliction bore the name of a saint; St Guy, St Vitus and St With were eponyms for chorea. St Hubert of Ardennes sponsored hydrophobia. St Anthony, St Benedict, St Martial and St Genevieve were traditionally linked with ergotism—a horrible plague. In the *Marmion* of Walter Scott, a recourse to a saint identified with a holy well may be seen:

> Thence to Saint Fillan's blessed well
> Whose spring can frenzied dreams dispel
> And the crazed brain restore.

And there were saints symbolized in art who sometimes cured hysteria or similar emotional conditions.[9] St Avertin and St John were mentioned in the prayers of thousands of epileptics who made annual pilgrimages to hallowed places in the hope that the demons which were blamed for their seizures would be expelled. St Valentine, the popular favourite of lovers in February, also became a patron of epileptics. Thomas Neogorgus, in *The Popish Kingdom*, illustrated this belief vividly:

> Saint Valentine, besides,
> To such as does his power despise
> The falling sickness, sends,
> And helps the man that to him cries.

MONTANUS TO DYMPNA

Dympna, a seventh-century martyr and saint, is another whose name is found in the history of mental health. She fled from Ireland to Gheel, Belgium, to escape the incestuous desire of her father, a petty pagan king of Oriel who wanted her to replace his deceased wife. Only fifteen years old at the time, Dympna was accompanied on the flight by her teacher and pastor, Gerebernus, the court jester and friends. Dympna's father discovered their whereabouts and, taking his soldiers, went to Belgium to persuade her to return home. When Gerebernus rebuked him for his wicked intentions, he had him put to death on the spot.

The brutal murder of her pastor intensified Dympna's determination to resist the insane, raging passion of her father. Infuriated by her rejection, he struck off her head. According to the legend, several of the 'lunatics' who observed these terrible events were 'shocked' into sanity. Later, Dympna became a special protectress of those with nervous disorders and more cures were attributed to her intercession. The reality of these cures could hardly be doubted since the key to any spontaneous recovery may be part of those intangible factors—auto-suggestion and faith.

Once the story of Dympna spread, large numbers of the insane visited Gheel, and seeing that they had no place to stay, citizens assumed the responsibility for them in their own homes. A shrine dedicated to the mentally ill, at Gheel, soon became world famous, where at one time as many as 1,500 patients lived with the kindly Belgians. Thus out of the martyrdom of a young lady grew a family-care plan, first a custom and now an organized programme in which the placement of patients bridges the wide gap between the mental hospital and outside society.

BIBLIOGRAPHY

1. Arthur Burton, 'On the Nature of Loneliness', *American Journal of Psychoanalysis*, 21 : 1, 1961, pp. 34-39.

2. Homer W. Smith, *Man and His Gods*, Grosset & Dunlap, New York, 1952, p. 382.

3. James J. Walsh, *The History of Nursing*, Kenedy, New York, 1929, p. 16.

4. Edward B. Pusey, Translator, the *Confessions of Saint Augustine*, Random House, New York, 1949, p. 166.

5. Marcus Dods, Translator, the *City of God*, Random House, New York, 1950, p. 846.

6. H. A. Overstreet, *The Mature Mind*, Norton, New York, 1949, p. 261.

7. D. Hack Tuke, Editor, *A Dictionary of Psychological Medicine*, Blakiston, Philadelphia, 1892, pp. 15-16.

8. Felix Martí-Ibáñez, 'Symbols and Medicine', *International Record of Medicine*, 173 : 2, 1960, p. 102.

9. Jean M. Charcot and Paul Richer, *Les Démoniaques dans l'Art*, Lecrosnier, Paris, 1887.

CHAPTER TWO

MOHAMMED TO AVERROES

In the Middle East, where the philosophy of brotherhood was born, a complex blend of people, said to be descendants of Sem, the eldest son of Noah, founded mental hospitals, outlined clinical syndromes, minimized barbaric restraints and prescribed drug therapy hundreds of years ago. There in a land enriched by institutions, haunted by history, torn by extremes of ancient cultures and medieval ways; of arid deserts and fertile fields; of sun-bathed beaches and snowcapped mountains; of narrow camel-paths and ultra-wide boulevards; there at the theosophic hub of the future grew an empire which was to leave an indelible imprint on the world of mental health.

The early settlers of this land along the storied Euphrates River possessed distinctive characteristics in both physique and personality. They had ruddy skins, average heights, powerful builds and dignified features; they had curious intellects, brave dispositions, tenacious traits and hospitable manners. They had the qualities of courageous soldiers who accepted death as a reality, neither sought nor feared; of master sailors who conquered the most treacherous waters; of skilful traders who penetrated the darkest areas and of devout missionaries who carried an intense faith to the farthest points.

Yet, despite their exciting participation in the mainstream of distant lands, the first natives, for the most part, lived on in the desert where time was nothing and tradition everything. Here, in humble abodes, the mothers dutifully educated the children while the fathers thrilled at the prospects of a birth of a camel, a delivery of a foal by a mare of noble breed or a triumph achieved by a poet. And for them, mental health could be found in an ancient proverb which increased awareness and offered this advice:

Men Are Four

He who knows not, and
Knows not he knows not—
He is a fool—shun him.

He who knows not, and
Knows he knows not—
He is a child—trust him.

He who knows, and
Knows not he knows—
He is asleep—wake him.

He who knows, and
Knows he knows—
He is wise—follow him.

At first, the people worshipped the stars and later many of them adopted Christianity, as evidenced by the fact that the town of Elhira contained numerous convents and monasteries; and King Ennomân-ben-el-Mondsir accepted the teachings of Christ just shortly before the coming of Mohammed.[1] However, those Arabs who fell beyond the pale were revengeful in their disposition and predatory in their habits; like present-day sociopaths, they gambled compulsively, gulped wine excessively, committed fornication, spoke ill of chaste women and bore false witness, and continued to do so on a large scale until the *Koran* abolished these vices.[2] Of a loose and sensual nature, these individuals could hardly have been in the best of mental health. They were dependent, labile and as a group seemed to lean instinctively to occultism and mysticism—those ancient practices which had blocked progress in mental health at every turn.

After centuries, religion (*superego*) evolved and soon dominated all walks of Arabian life, including mental health. Since it did not cheapen religion to accentuate its meaning on personal comfort and absence of anxiety, the art of psychotherapy quickly reoriented itself to the creeds. But the creeds clashed, and instead of aborting the fossilization of ideas they created an irreparable crevice in dogmas. Out of this schism emerged Arianism, Nestorianism and Monophysitism, theoretical systems that completely absorbed the best minds with abstractions and theological nuances and sadly disregarded mental health concepts. Added to this was the weaving of a 'carpet curtain' around the country, making it virtually impenetrable to outside ideas.

Such was the psychologic climate in the pre-Islamic centuries, centuries which started the ball of politico-ecclesiastic dissension rolling. It was an atmosphere reminiscential of the days of Origen, and remained so until Alexandria opened its port on the way *to becoming* the mental health centre of an ethnically many-coloured Graeco-Roman-Arabic world. But *to become* was a slow tantalizing process, and one laments the fact that after all of the deep, serious study, basic religious questions remained unanswered and continued to disrupt the course of history. During these years religious doctrines appeared as numerous as the stars in the sky, and one theological epoch after another passed through a period of violent insurrection. George B. Shaw related the problem to an amusing parallel in science:[3]

'Let the Churches ask themselves why there is no revolt against the dogmas of mathematics though there is one against the dogmas of religion. It is not that mathematical dogmas are more comprehensible. The law of inverse squares is as incomprehensible to the common man as the Athanasian Creed. It is not that science is free from legends, witchcraft, miracles, biographic boosting of quacks as heroes and saints, and of barren scoundrels as explorers and discoverers. On the contrary, the iconography and hagiology of Scientism are as copious as they are mostly squalid. But no student of science has yet been taught that specific gravity consists in the belief that Archimedes jumped out of his bath and ran naked through the streets of Syracuse shouting Eureka, Eureka, or that the law of inverse squares must be discarded if anyone can prove that Newton was

never in an orchard in his life. When some unusually conscientious or enterprising bacteriologist reads the pamphlets of
William Jenner, and discovers that they might have been written by
an ignorant but curious and and observant nurserymaid, and could
not possibly have been written by any person with a scientifically
trained mind, he does not feel that the whole edifice of science
has collapsed and crumbled, and that there is no such thing as
smallpox. It may come to that yet; for hygiene, as it forces its
way into our schools, is being taught as falsely as religion is
taught there; but in mathematics and physics the faith is still
kept pure, and you may take the law and leave the legends without suspicion of heresy. Accordingly, the tower of the mathe-
matician stands unshaken whilst the temple of the priest rocks to
its foundation.'

Paraphrasing Shaw's extraordinary method of logic, a similar
analogy between *mental health* and *medicine* would run something
like this: Let the *colleges* ask themselves why there is no revolt
against the dogmas of *medicine* though there is one against the
dogmas of *mental health*. It is not that the medical dogmas are
more comprehensible. The *all-or-none* law is as incomprehensible
to the common man as the *Jungian Theory*. It is not that
experimentation is free from legends, witchcraft, miracles, biographic boostings of quacks as heroes and saints, and of barren
scoundrels as explorers and discoverers. On the contrary, the
iconography and hagiology of *Empiricism* are as copious as they
are mostly squalid. But no student of *experimentation* has yet
been taught that *insight* consists in the belief that *Graham Wallas*
jumped out of his steam cabinet and ran naked through the
streets of *London* shouting *ah-ah, ah-ah*, or that the *all-or-none
law* must be discarded if anyone can prove that *Edgar Adrian*
was never kicked by a horse. When some unusually conscientious
or enterprising *pathologist* reads the pamphlets of *Jonas Salk* and
discovers that they might have been written by an ignorant but
curious and observant *organ grinder*, and could not possibly have
been written by any person with an *experimentally* trained mind,
he does not feel that the whole edifice of *experimentation* has

collapsed and crumbled, and that there is no such thing as *polio*. It may come to that yet; *mental health*, as it forces its way into our schools, is being taught as falsely as *psychology* is taught there; but in *medicine* and *physiology* the faith is still kept pure, and you may take the law and leave the legends without suspicion of heresy. Accordingly, the tower of the *physician* stands unshaken whilst the temple of the *psychologist* rocks to its foundation.

MIND OF MOHAMMED

So much for the digression and epilogue. Now let us return to the chronological development of Arabia, where the different religions—too spiritual for the contemporary mind—began to disperse and make way for new habits. Rejecting primitive beliefs, the Arabs then preached against sun-worship, doused the fire temples, ridiculed ceremonies, tore up fetishes and condemned superstition. They then searched for a faith which embodied the thinking of their beloved ancestors and at the same time applied a relatively simple principle of one God-head. Thus, in a climate with its attendant sentimental increment, Mohammed—an incredibly dynamic personality with a hungering ego—launched the era of Islam.

Mohammed, 'the praised one', came into the world at Mecca, the only child of Abdallah (Servant of God) and Amina, of the tribe of Koreish. When his beloved and handsome father took Amina for a wife, two hundred disappointed maidens supposedly died of broken hearts. Legends added that his mother suffered no pains of labour, and the moment Mohammed saw the light of day, he raised his eyes heavenward and exclaimed:

> *La ilahā illa-l-Lah;*
> *Muhammadun rasulu-l-Lah.*

> There is no god but God;
> Mohammed is the prophet of God.

The followers of Islam also claimed that other omens and strange portents took place at the time of his birth. Lake Sawa turned into an arid wasteland; the sacred fire of Zoroaster that the Magi kept burning uninterruptedly for hundreds of years suddenly went out; the idols tumbled down; the massive palace of King Khosrau of Persia rocked so violently from top to bottom that some of the towers fell.

Before Mohammed was three months old, his father died and his mother grieved so much that her breasts dried up. Halima, wife of a Bedouin shepherd, then cared for the infant, only to return him after two years because he had epileptic seizures. At the age of six, Mohammed lost his mother and then went to live with his paternal grandfather. Sometime later his uncle Abu Talib adopted him and trained him to be a merchant. While on a business trip to Syria, the two of them visited a Nestorian monastery, and the boy left there impressed with ideas that remained with him for the rest of his life. Even as a youth he displayed excessive religiosity, and it has been said that his epileptoid predisposition had much to do with this morbid trait in his personality.

Though limited in education, Mohammed showed signs of a remarkable memory and good judgment. A keen student of human nature, he also possessed a poetic bent and an excellent command of the Bible and the Arabic folklore. These and other qualities he demonstrated in an assignment as managing agent to Kadijah, a twice-widowed woman fifteen years his senior for whom he conducted commercial affairs so well that a romance resulted which culminated in their marriage. The financial security and complete solvency afforded by Kadijah's wealth then permitted Mohammed to direct his abundant psychic energy to theological contemplation. Soon the idea of a new purified faith absorbed his mind so thoroughly that it motivated his every act. With this religion, he hoped to abolish the moral dilemmas, pharisaic deceits, multiple idolatries and spiritual complexities of that time. He made an all-out effort to bring his people together, since he felt strongly that the desperately-sought-for unity of Arabian society could not be realized if the tribes continued to oppose one another.

MOHAMMED TO AVERROES

Beginning with Adam, Mohammed reviewed the respective missions of Noah, Abraham, Moses and Christ, and he concluded that man presently needed another prophet to return the heretics to the oneness of God. Then in the ninth month of the Arabian year, the month of Ramadan, he made an annual retreat to a cave on Mt Hara, where he fasted ascetically and meditated intensively. It was under such self-imposed hardships that his vivid imagination broke from reality and he visualized the archangel Gabriel producing a silken cloth inscribed with these words:

> Read! said the angel.
> I know not how to read! he replied.
> Read, repeated the angel.

According to Arabic tradition, the commands of Gabriel illumined the mind of the previously illiterate prophet with celestial light and he understood the decrees on the cloth well enough to enact them into the *Koran*. His devoted wife; her uncle, Waraka; an ardent nephew, Ali; a faithful servant, Zaid and a prominent citizen, Abu Bekr, numbered among his first converts. When the news of Mohammed's revelation and his faith leaked out, many ridiculed him openly; others charged him with insanity and some tried to assassinate him; but he foiled all attempts on his life by going into seclusion under the protection of his uncle and remained hidden for several years.

During the early days, Mohammed and a small group of disciples encountered strong opposition and bitter persecution wherever they preached, and in order to survive he had to draw the sword and launch the first of many bloody affairs. Forced to again leave Mecca in 622, he went to Medina on what has been called the *Hegira* or flight, and then his personality showed drastic changes in so far as the high-pressure drives of aggression and affection. First, Mohammed's appetite for battle seemed insatiable whether it was a fratricidal fight or a clash with strangers, and next, his thirst for love could no longer be contained. In his revision of the *Koran*, he granted himself various privileges in marriage; and going from one amour to another, he rationalized his sensuous habits by claiming that they were a part of a divine mission which, in fact, reversed his original professed revelations. No one can deny that he practised what he believed, since at his death Mohammed's harem had increased upwards to nine wives, with Ayesha the favourite. Four of the women had equal legal status; and the others lived merely as concubines.

Biographies of Mohammed are, on the whole, replete with fictitious details, anecdotes and legends and, therefore, unreliable. In all probability, the Koranic commentators who wrote in the century after his death provided the most dependable source for highlights of his life. As far as can be determined, the appearance of the great Arabian leader was neither imposing nor pleasing; but it was inspiring. Average in height, he had broad shoulders, deep chest, powerful build, large head, high brow, round and ruddy face, wide mouth and long, aquiline nose. His dark, burning eyes reflected a peculiar magnetic charm, and a turban covered his thick, black, curly hair; his beard remained free of grey until he neared old age. He had between his shoulders a prominent birthmark which his followers regarded as a holy sign of prophecy.

Concerning Mohammed the person, many writers expressed an extreme hatred or an exaggerated love for him. Martin Luther characterized him as 'a devil and first-born child of Satan'. Friedrich Spanheim and Barthélemy d'Herbelot described him as a 'wicked impostor' and a 'dastardly liar'. Humphrey Prideaux stamped him as a 'wilful deceiver'. Such indiscriminate abuse lacked factual support. Samuel M. Zwemer gathered together the various opinions and attempted to present an unbiased evaluation of Mohammed and concluded that the judgment of scholars, however harsh, rested on evidence which 'comes from the lips and pens of his own devoted adherents. . . . And the followers of the prophet can scarcely complain if, even on such evidence, the verdict of history goes against him.'[4]

Arrogant and strong-willed in most ways, Mohammed none

the less lived simply and frugally in a miserable hut he called home. His bed consisted of straw with a pillow of palm leaves covered by leather. The recurring motif running through his mind seemed to be alternately comic and pathetic; he needed to be accepted—not just accepted—but well accepted. He was strangely contradictory; wanting the impossible, that is, acceptance by all, he was generous, kind, loyal and tender on the one hand, but cunning, cowardly and deceitful on the other. Aloys Sprenger related his behaviour to epilepsy, or to a 'paroxysm of cataleptic insanity', accompanied by visions, profuse perspiration and a state of complete exhaustion from which there was no immediate recovery.[5]

To sum up, the religion propagated by Mohammed embraced several major concepts: Monotheistic to the core, it denied any idea of a Trinity then or ever after. Success in the fanatical religious wars convinced Mohammed that he would be the last to receive a prophetic office from the one God. This final word of the Creator to man spelled out in the sacred Moslem book gave the new faith a definitive quality not found in the contemporary religions.

The Islamic system of demonology, which evolved from the Satanic (*id*) theory of the Jews, represented a limitless reservoir of superstitions. On the one side, there were good angels (*superego*)—infinite beings—who were created of light and each for benevolent purposes. On the other, there were bad angels (*id*)—finite creatures—who were born of fire and each for malevolent purposes. The daily actions of an Islamite were thought of in terms of the *Kismet*, which considered fate to be immune to change once God had decided. Any attempts to reconcile this belief with free will brought controversies that were similar in part to those disputes which raged among the Christian theologians on the subject of grace. Some points of the Islamic doctrine of fatalism still explain the rigid and stagnant way of life in most Arabian lands where this belief impugns any concept of recovery in mental or physical disorders. Dying for Allah or his prophet means going straight to a paradise where the soul enjoys a constant round of sensuous, worldly pleasures. Contradictory as it is, women were regarded as having no immortal souls; hence, they never shared in the joys of heaven! At least one freethinking hedonist, Omar Khayyám, did not exclude them from an 'earthly paradise', as is obvious in this oft-quoted, alluring quatrain from his *Rubáiyát*:

> A Book of Verses underneath the Bough,
> A Jug of Wine, a Loaf of Bread—and Thou
>   Beside me singing in the Wilderness—
> Oh, Wilderness were Paradise enow!

What Mohammed and his successors accomplished catapulted the people of ancient Arabia out of the realm of obscurity and into the international spotlight, and by doing so carried their mental health ideas to other countries. The Bedouins, semi-nomadic tribes now strongly united and spurred by religious ardour and rich booty, subdued North Africa, conquered West Asia and formed a kingdom in Spain. Yet 'the crescent never rounded to the full', for the crack Arab legions were repulsed in the East at Constantinople (718) and stopped completely in the West at Tours (732) when Charles Martel won the title of the 'Hammer' by routing the army of Abd-er-Rahman.

Frustrated in their attempt to control Europe, the Arabs then divided into two empires more or less hostile to each other. Bagdad, the capital of the Caliphate in the East inhabited by the Saracens, became one of the richest cities in the world. Cordova, on the peninsula of Spain, served as the leading centre for the West where the Moors held sway. Populated with one million people, this city had paved roads, street lighting, hundreds of baths, elementary schools for children, exquisite minarets and, above all, a sound mental health programme.

With the caliphs in power, art, literature and poetry reached a peak of development in a span of time which the so-called 'barbarians' translated and helped to introduce what the Greeks learned about mental health to medieval Europe. In fact, many of the old works would have been lost for ever had not the

Moslems preserved and edited them. They further improved astronomy, mathematics, geometry, geography and history and perfected the study of algebra, borrowed from India; they also exchanged ideas with China and excelled all others in medicine:

'Looking back we may say that Islamic medicine and science reflected the light of the Hellenic sun, when its day had fled, and that they shone like a moon, illuminating the darkest night of the European Middle Ages; that some bright stars lent their own light, and that moon and stars alike faded at the dawn of a new day—the Renaissance. Since they had their share in the direction and introduction of that great movement, it may reasonably be claimed that they are with us yet.'[6]

ARABIAN ALIENISTS

In so far as mental health, the Islams proposed a blissful union of science and religion. To do this they applied pithy maxims: 'Science lights the road to Paradise. Take ye knowledge even from the lips of an infidel. The ink of the scholar is more holy than the blood of the martyr.' And in the 37th Chapter of the *Koran*: 'Allah created you and all your actions, *Mektoub* (book), it is written'. Such sententious sayings alone do not insure progress in a theocratic culture that still spelled metaphysics in bold-faced letters. Human dissections were forbidden, and physicians never (reputedly) examined unclothed women. Opportunities for advanced study and research simply did not exist, for education revolved around the *Koran*, a book considered the source of all truth.

Notwithstanding these handicaps, Moslem growth was rapid and learning prodigious. At the height of Arabian culture, the mentally ill were studied, described and treated objectively. In the West, European medicine submitted to the medieval satanic theories; but in the East, Islamic medicine clung to the ancient Greek teachings. The torch, ignited by Hippocrates, was carried proudly by the Arabian doctors who, themselves, had tolerant understanding of psychological conditions.

Najab ud din Unhammad, a seldom-mentioned psychiatrist of the mid-eighth century, authored a remarkable paper (*Asbab wa Ullamut*) on symptoms, classification and treatment of mental disorders. Nafis ibn Awaz wrote a commentary in 1450 about this treatise; and Muhammad Akbar translated it into Persian in the seventeenth century. Najab had defined insanity as 'a state of agitation and distraction, with alteration and loss of reason, caused by weakness or disease affecting the brain'. All in all, Unhammad listed nine classes of psychopathology and outlined separate entities:[7]

Souda a Tabee (febrile delirium), subdivided into *Souda* and *Janoon*, was a type of dementia in most respects. Out of contact with the environment, these patients ran around denuded and untidy, laughed like children and showed critical impairment in memory. Some resembled melancholia—intense anxiety—with a constant dread of approaching evil. Others lost control of their arms and legs, leaped about and pounded the ground. When *Souda* reached a chronic state, it ended in *Janoon* (agitated reaction) characterized by insomnia, restlessness and taciturnity, broken at times by beast-like roars.

Murrae Souda (obsessive compulsive) applied to those with morbid anxiety and who were 'constantly full of doubts'. Victims of this disorder had downcast eyes, thin faces and weak pulses. Their treatment included the following recommendations: 'Do nothing to agitate the brain, avoid violent purgatives, give nourishing drinks, also flesh and fish. Patients should live in a place where the temperature is mild, and be surrounded by many trees and roses.' If these measures failed to effect a recovery, then venesection would be tried on a small scale so as not to add to the debility.

Malikholia a Maraki (involutional psychotic reaction) was explained by Unhammad in terms of humoral pathology, where the humours and body heat passed from the limbs to the brain. As the heat (*Marak*) ascended, it destroyed the soul and clouded the intellect, thus impairing reasoning and reducing action. Some patients became choleric and violent, others, tranquil and serene.

Simeon Stylites

Augustine of Hippo

Treatment depended upon whether there were signs of inflammation or not; for the former, bleeding and milk was ordered; for the latter, a high caloric diet.

Diwangi, a generic concept, embraced four subdivisions of disorders. The first category, *Kutrib* (paranoid disorders), derived its name from a small animal who was ever on the move, to represent the restlessness present. Since the same word meant jackal, it also referred to the howling which was heard in certain patients. Suspicious and wild, patients were often seen hiding among the tombs and in the woods during the day, emerging out only at night. Sad and melancholic, at times they lacerated themselves with thorns and stones. Though patients might be bled at the onset, the most important treatment here was to produce motor activity by occupation or games. If this therapy failed, water would be dashed repeatedly on their heads; and they were never permitted to sit in the dark.

The second form of *Diwangi* used the familiar Greek title of *Mania*, the Arabic equivalent being *Janoon Tabee* or *Janoon Haeeg*. Those afflicted with this malady attacked others, tore clothing and destroyed furniture and reacted like maniacs. The third kind, called *Daul-Kulb*, resembled hydrophobia where patients fawned like a *Kulb*, which is Arabic for dog. And if they bit another person, the one bitten soon died with symptoms similar to those seen in victims of rabid animals. The fourth type, known as *Sadar*, described a mania associated with 'swelling of the brain'. For this condition the first reference to mechanical restraint was made, in that the patient's hands and feet were bound to control hyperactivity, to rest the brain and to prevent injury to self and others.

Haziyan (sociopathic disturbance) designated an antisocial personality disturbance characterized mainly by poor judgment and behavioural reactions. This group included three states: (1) *Mibda a illut dimagh*, (2) *Mibda a illut Marak* and (3) *Bukharat Had*. The next major classes, *Raoonut* and *Himak*, seemed much like the foregoing in many ways and, therefore, require no further elaboration.

Ishk (depressive reaction) gets its name from the word *ishka*, a creeping plant which wraps around a tree and kills it slowly. This disorder was described rather well as a condition precipitated by external factors. Grief-stricken over the loss of a love object, patients sought solitude and a place to cry alone in an effort to reduce their anxiety. According to Najab, the illness came in two forms: *Haram* due to impure love and *Pak* caused by pure love but excessive venery. Those so afflicted must be amused, kept happy by stimulating motor activity and watched closely lest they try suicide. Marriage was considered as the best remedy.

Nisyan (amnesia) simply meant loss of memory usually due to age or deterioration. Unhammad had no special therapy for it other than mnemonic devices which usually failed and then he shrugged his shoulders and said: '*Ahna fineesh saad ahk*', meaning 'I can't help you'. No need to detail the cocktail-sounding subdivision of *Nisyan*, that is, *Zikr*, *Fikr* and *Takhil*.

In the same century as Unhammad, streams of an ethnic current flowed into Bagdad and brought in top medical men to vitalize the caliphs' courts. Among the physicians were such famous names as Bakhtischu, Masawayh and Honain. Jibril Bakhtischu, son of Jurjis, successfully treated a wife of Harun-al-Rashid, the idealized caliph of *Arabian Nights*. It was said that she suffered a mental disorder and the doctor 'cured' her with intimidation and reproach, techniques of psychotherapy however crude.

Honain translated a number of medical books from Greek to Syrian and was paid in gold equal to the weight of each text completed for Rashid. Though these works were obscured by rendering them from one language to another, they presented the Arabs with an opportunity to continue the tradition of Hippocrates, Aristotle and Galen. Isaac, the son of Honain, became an even more respected medical writer and teacher who trained a number of physicians in his day, and three to four centuries later his texts continued to enjoy widespread use.[8]

MOHAMMED TO AVERROES

Rhazes spent a number of years travelling and entertaining harems with anecdotes and lute-playing before his wanderings brought him into contact with alchemists who aroused an interest first in medicine and then in mental health. Studying the subject intently, he rose from a roustabout matinee idol to be one of the greatest clinicians of that day. His reputation grew so fast that the caliph asked him to select a site for a huge hospital in Bagdad, and Rhazes, a most original thinker, suggested that pieces of raw flesh be placed throughout the city to determine the purest location, and where the meat decomposed the least he recommended that ground be broken for the building. Nearly one millennium later, Louis Pasteur carried a similar little experiment to a dramatic and wonderful conclusion.

As head of the beautifully appointed Bagdad institution, Rhazes set aside what may be termed a psychiatric unit in a general hospital today wherein the mentally ill received the best and kindliest care. Probably aware of the time when he trod the primrose path, Rhazes then dedicated himself completely to the sick; he insisted that a physician's energy ought to be devoted exclusively to the patient and not diverted by active participation in music, poetry, politics, fictional writing or the like.

Despite the fact that his professional advice was constantly in demand, Rhazes found time to do much clinical writing. Over one hundred works flowed from his pen, of which twelve dealt with alchemy. One of his main papers on alchemy (*De Spiritibus et Corporibus*) was quoted by Roger Bacon. A thesis differentiating measles and smallpox rated as a cameo classic. The *Katib Al Hāwi*, a comprehensive work of twenty-five volumes, was translated into Latin (*Liber Continens*) and endured to be part of a medical *bibliothèque* in Paris in the fourteenth century. Another sixteenth-century copy is in the Garrett collection at Princeton University. An Arabic edition of the *Continens* of Rhazes published recently in India may be found in the John J. White Department of the Cleveland Public Library.[9]

Though the top Arabian medical man contributed few new ideas to mental health, his aphorisms demonstrated a sharp sensitivity to psychogenic factors. Time and again he employed prestige suggestions to influence and motivate patients towards better adjustment, for instance when he applied an amusing bit of psychology to help Amir Mansur of the house of Saman who could not walk because of badly swollen feet. After the amir was confortably seated in a steam bath, Rhazes quickly drew a dagger from his cloak and the frightened and enraged ruler jumped to his feet, the first time he was able to stand since his illness. Needless to say, the doctor made a hurried exit but soon wrote to the king and explained the treatment. In his letter, he attributed the difficulty to a weakness in 'natural caloric'. To remedy such a disorder by the conventional means then would have been a protracted affair, so Rhazes ordered heat and deliberately stirred up Mansur to produce more 'caloric' (utilization of caloric energy) in his system. The explanation pleased the monarch immensely and he gave Rhazes a hand-maiden, a male slave, two hundred asses laden with corn, and several smaller gifts.

As a rule, Rhazes and the other Arab doctors seldom had to be paid this way. Blessed with a shrewd business sense, they asked for their fees at a time when the illness reached its peak. Euricius Cordus, humanist physician and epigrammatic poet, also recognized this same mechanism in his patients and summed it up in a verse which has been translated by Chauncey Leake:[10]

God and the Doctor we alike adore
When on the brink of danger, not before.
The danger past, both are alike requited
God is forgotten and the doctor slighted.

Avicenna, or Ibn Sina, came from Efsene, a small village near Bokhara, and practised medicine at Hamadan. Known as the Prince of Physicians, he presented an interesting study in contrasts. According to legends, he possessed an encyclopedic fund of knowledge, able to recite the *Koran* at the age ten, and mastered history, mathematics, philosophy and poetry while still a teenager. But when he reached adulthood, he rollicked and philandered with the girls and travelled the festive circuits in the best playboy manner. A fashionable sensualist, he failed to heed the Arabic maxim: 'The most harmful thing for an elderly man is to have a clever cook and a pretty maid'. Stricken ill, he treated himself but died at the apex of a promising career, probably from gastric carcinoma. Epitaphists who knew him added this grim inscription:

> His physic did not save his body, and
> His metaphysic could not save his soul.

Writers disagreed as to his precise role in the development of medico-psychological matters. Dante ranked him with the best. Sir William Osler called him 'one of the greatest names in the history of medicine'. William Whewell considered him 'the Hippocrates and Galen of the Arabians'. Gregory Zilboorg termed his achievements paradoxical. A medieval prodigy with a rich background in medicine, Avicenna still did not add any original ideas to the study of mental disorders. Actually, he achieved fame mainly by a brilliant style of writing and an excellent arrangement of subject-matter. Reviewing a French translation, Noël Mailloux, of the University of Montreal, wrote:[11]

'It is well known that, in devoting the sixth book of his monumental work, *As-Sifa* (*The Cure*), to the consideration of psychological problems, Avicenna has exerted a deep and lasting influence on all the great scholastic thinkers of the Middle Ages, for many of them found there a powerful incentive for writing original commentaries on Aristotle's *De Anima* and elaborating on ethics, based on an empirical and dynamic conception of human nature rather than on legalistic formalism. In those days no one pretended to become a moralist without first acquiring a profound knowledge of psychology.'

Avicenna's *Canon of Medicine*, an accomplishment of great magnitude, proved to be a daring attempt to synthesize the

Greek and Arabic healing arts and served as a standard of European medicine for five centuries.[12] Among his tributes, he appreciated the influence of the mind over the body. In this respect, he was credited with effecting a cure in a young man somewhat similar to the case treated by Erasistratos in antiquity. During an examination, Avicenna held the patient's pulse and at the same time tried a primitive method of word association. Requesting an aide to recite the names of a number of towns in the districts, the doctor noted a fluttering pulsation with the mention of a certain village. Avicenna followed up this lead and had someone list homes and addresses in that definite area. And when hearing a particular street number the youth's pulse, 'the messenger who does not lie', increased in rate. Avicenna inferred that the patient loved a girl living there and prescribed marriage as the suitable treatment. He even recommended the propitious day for the wedding. So commenting upon the operation of psychogenic factors, the noted Arabian medico-philosopher said: 'At times the confidence of the patient in the physician has more influence over the disease than the medicine given for it'.

Despite the penetrating insight displayed in the above situations, Avicenna had some glaring failings elsewhere. In his candid opinion, to be in love meant to be mentally ill. Then too, he overextended the concept of the mind, considered it as a phenomenon which could modify or influence others at a distance. Such an idea yielded to the dominant mystical belief (witchcraft) that man sometimes worked harm on his enemies in this manner. Still another of Avicenna's shortcomings slowed progress to a creeping pace, when with syllogistic confidence he set men discussing ludicrous questions as: Why was the brain located in the head? Would it not be logical to have the stomach lie behind the mouth? What if the breasts grew on the abdomen? And why were calves on the back of legs instead of the front?[13]

CANDLE FROM CORDOVA

Soon after Avicenna's time, a powerful secret order swept across the Middle East like a desert whirlwind. Led by the notorious

Hasan ibn-al-Sabbah, the members of this Islamic society indulged in hashish (hemp) before launching a savage wave of aggression upon the Christians. Known by the Arabic name of Hashshashin (assassin), the murderous sect, while under the influence of the Oriental drug, carried out a campaign of death and terror well into the thirteenth century.

Averroes was born in Cordova, the 'cradle of philosophers'. Sometimes called Ibn Rushd, he studied medicine with the objective-minded Avenzoar at Seville and, like his teacher, acidly criticized charlatanry and superstition until he made the enmity of the orthodox Moslems who regarded such criticism as an attack upon the mysticism of the *Koran*. Not dismayed by the opposition, Averroes maintained his position, wrote with authority and skill and was called to serve as physician-in-ordinary to the caliphs. This fact alone returned to Arabian medicine some of the prestige and respect it had had in Greece.

In philosophy, Averroes influenced Judaic and Christian tradition far more than the Islamic religion. Yet his basic doctrines never broke with the pantheism and rationalism of the Moorish system, for Averroes italicized some points of Aristotle which sabotaged Church dogma, such as the denial of the Creation and the belief that the human soul was corruptible. Consequently, the schoolmen were obliged to refute him.

In psychology, the Arabian commentator concluded that a 'double truth' existed, that is, a truth based upon theological revelation could be decried by philosophy, and a truth grounded on philosophical reasoning could be rejected by theology: *What is true in theology may be false in philosophy, and vice versa.* Such a principle had some bearing on mental health, in that it allowed theologians to study controversial issues without developing guilt feelings or fear of losing their souls, and thus opened a vista of scientific inquiry at a time when mystical current and religious fervour flowed carelessly.

In law, Averroes presided as judge in Seville and Cordova and later became governor of a province. At about the age of thirty he ran into a wave of psychosocial fanaticism, was charged with heresy unjustly and exiled to a small Jewish settlement near his birthplace. Fortuitously, he soon received a pardon and had his civil rights restored, which he kept for forty years until Abu-Yusuf al-Mansur, of the Almohade dynasty, banished him to Morocco, where he died at the age of seventy-two.

Most of the Arab doctors, of the period studied thus far, had a relatively enlightened view about mental disorders. In what appeared to be an early interpretation of schizophrenic reaction, they described patients who withdrew from their environment and remained so for months or years.

Some writers gave the Arabs credit for opening the first complete mental hospitals. Rabbi Benjamin of Tudela, a twelfth-century traveller who generally told the truth, supported this view.[14] Except for the use of the chains at the *House of Grace*, the Moslems applied modern therapeutic methods for the mentally ill from admission to discharge.[15]

'. . . there are about sixty physicians' stores which are provided from the Caliph's house with drugs and whatever else may be required. . . . Here is a building which is called *Dar-al-Maristan*, where they keep charge of the demented people who have become insane in the towns through the great heat of the summer, and they chain each of them in iron chains until their reason becomes restored to them in the wintertime. Whilst they abide there, they are provided with food from the house of the Caliph, and when their reason is restored they are dismissed and each of them goes to his house and his home. Money is given to those that have stayed in the hospices on their return to their homes. Every month the officers of the Caliph inquire and investigate whether they have regained their reason, in which case they are discharged. All this the Caliph does out of charity to those that come to the city of Bagdad, whether they be sick or insane. . . .'

One of the best-known institutions in Arab lands was the Mansuri Hospital of Cairo which consisted of four large court-yards with designated sections for various diseases that included a wing for mental disorders. Storytellers drifted everywhere among the patients and administered their primitive but effective brand of psychotherapy. They applied a crude form of biblio-therapy by encouraging the sick to select books on a wide range of subjects that were made available in the hospital library. Mansuri Hospital reflected an almost collegiate atmosphere with relaxed groups of men and women walking around the grounds, lectures and seminars everywhere, and numerous social gather-ings that helped open the road to recovery.

Outside of the infrequent use of phlebotomy and purgation, the insane under the Arabs received better care than in the good old days of the lancet in England. Patients' appetite were whetted with sweets, dried fruits, grapes, apples and water-melons. Soft music, beautiful gardens, majestic trees and fragrant shrubs created an atmosphere intended to induce relaxation and sleep. Shaik al Ajab described the prevailing humanitarian attitude which even surpassed that of Philippe Pinel in Paris, William Tuke in York and Vincenzo Chiarugi in Florence many centuries later:

'Be it known that of all remedies, to strengthen the heart and brain is the safest and most sure, by which means the mind and action are guided aright. Do nothing to frighten a patient, and let him select his own employment. Make the senses a special subject of treatment, and occasionally give stimulants. Rest and fresh air are required for the miserable men afflicted with insanity. They should be shown every possible kindness; in fact, they are to be treated by those under whose care they are placed as if they were their own offspring, so as to encourage them to place confidence in their caretakers, and communicate their feelings and sufferings to them. This will be at least a relief to those unfortunates, and a charity in the eyes of God.'

By the twelfth century the Arabs introduced puppet shows to entertain the sick. A hundred years afterwards, a Moslem physician of Jewish or Christian origin, al-Khuza'i al-Mawsili, wrote about a highly developed specimen of shadow play under the title, *Tayf al-Khayal fi Ma'rifat Khayal al-Zill* (*Phantoms of the Imagination on the knowledge of Shadow Play*), to add to the techniques which, in many ways, anticipated projective doll play, psychodrama and puppetry, modern methods for research, diagnosis and psychotherapy.

The spiral of mental health progress in the Middle East continued spinning upward, as it were, until the Mongols over-ran Bagdad. Then the decline that followed was almost as swift as the rise and seemed complete and irrevocable when the bellicose Arabs lost their flaming swords before the increased European pressure in the West and the truculent Genghis Khan in the East. After Khan his grandson, Hulagu, moved in (1258) and sacked the country so savagely that the rich irrigated land returned to the desert. Thus, another culture that had a transient and a fleeting impact on the broad scene of history fell and with it ended one of the most promising chapters in the book of mental health.

BIBLIOGRAPHY

1. Frederick C. Beach, 'Arabia', *Americana*, 1 : 1, 1903.
2. Philip K. Hitti, *History of the Arabs*, Macmillan, New York, 1951.
3. George B. Shaw, *Back to Methuselah*, Constable, London, 1921, p. 89.
4. Samuel M. Zwemer, *Islam, A Challenge to Faith*, Student Volunteer Movement, New York, 1907.
5. Aloys Sprenger. *Das Leben und die Lehre des Mohammed*, Nicolai'-sche, Berlin, 1861.
6. Max Meyerhof, 'Science and Medicine', *The Legacy of Islam*, Oxford University Press, 1931, p. 354.
7. J. G. Balfour, 'An Arab Physician on Insanity', *Journal of Mental Science*, July, 1876.
8. Gregory Zilboorg, *A History of Medical Psychology*, Allen & Unwin, London, 1941, p. 120.
9. Zakariyya Rāzi, *Kitabu'l Hāwi Fi't-Tibb*, Osmania, Hyderabad-Deccan, 1955.
10. Otto L. Bettmann, *A Pictorial History of Medicine*, Thomas, Springfield, 1956, p. 139.
11. Jan Bakos, Editor, *Psychologie d'Ibn Sina*, Académie Tchecoslovaque des Sciences, Prague, 1956.

12. William C. Dampier, *A History of Science*, Cambridge University, Cambridge, 1949, p. 75.
13. Ritchie Calder, *Medicine and Man*, Allen & Unwin, London, 1958, p. 75.
14. Leo W. Schwarz, Editor, *Great Ages and Ideas of the Jewish People*, Random House, New York, 1956, p. 303.
15. Marcus N. Adler, Translator, *Itinerary of Rabbi Benjamin of Tudela*, Frowde, London, 1907, p. 38.

CHAPTER THREE

ABELARD TO AQUINAS

A number of signs anticipated the rise of the medieval monk to replace the ancient doctor in the emporium of mental health. Scanning the literature for pertinent data in the twelfth century, we find that Michael Psellus completed a bulky 'psychomedical' volume which sadly omitted the positive ideas in the field up to that time, and, instead, gave a detailed account of the hierarchy of demons and how they set traps to snare the human soul. The author himself may have had psychotic episodes. To him belonged the singular honour of having been the first to 'codify' the ancient lore of demonology which became an unshakable basis for the medieval treatment of mental disorders.[1]

The discovery of the science of endocrinology, late in the same century that Psellus died, even failed to impress the demonologists. Few, if any, of them noticed that Roger Frugardi of Salerno in 1180 had observed that goitre patients could be treated effectively with ashes of seaweed and sponges that were high in iodine content.[2]

Irnerius, a Bolognese jurist and contemporary of Psellus, made a noble attempt to slow the decline and prevent the complete surrender to demonology by reviving the study of the old Roman law. With his *Summa Codicis* he tried hard to systematize the scattered decrees of the ancients. And like Justinian, the famed sixth-century emperor, he too considered the mentally ill from a juridical and comprehensible frame of reference as spelled out in the renowned *Corpus Juris Civilis*:[3]

'It was clearly stated in the Law that an insane person could not make any valid contract. This prohibition was especially maintained in the matter of wills and marriages. With regard to wills, every possible contingency was covered by the Law; for example, the case of a will made before the insanity, during the insanity, during an intermittent spell of sanity and, finally, a will in the making at the moment of the onset of insanity. Mental incompetence was declared to be an absolute obstacle to the validity of a marriage contract, but to have no effect on a marriage contracted before its appearance. Insanity was, however, in extreme cases considered a justifying cause for divorce. The Law covered, in detail, the matter of the appointment, duties and problems of curators or guardians of the insane. Finally, the Law also exempted the insane in the sphere of crime and penalty and penalized, on the other hand, those who neglected to properly care for insane members of the family.'

PETER ABELARD

Peter Abélard was another representative of that same era who also showed a realistic view of mental disorders. Not concerned with the legal aspects, he simply debunked the idea that the devil caused insanity, but the manner in which he expressed his view was so bitter that the Catholic Church denounced him, after Bernard of Clairvaux had complained to Rome. Had Abélard presented his idea of mental illness in a more subtle manner, no telling how it might have been received. This, however, he could not do because of his own mental health. His personality and some details of his romance with Héloïse provide an interesting clinical study.

Bernard had once described Abélard as being *'vir bellator ab adolescentia'*; and this he seemed to be if his numerous personality clashes are any index. But with his brilliant mind and eloquent speech, Abélard soon established and outstanding record as a teacher, a reputation which, at the age of thirty-seven, won for him the assignment to tutor Héloïse, the seventeen-year-old niece of Canon Fulbert of the cathedral school. Shy, frightened and lonely, Héloïse found in Abélard a man of erudition and stature who could give her self-confidence. From the start of their relationship it was obvious that she would never be the pious intellect of her imago, yet few can deny her one honour, that of the love goddess of her generation.

In *Historia Calamitatum*, Abélard disclosed his conflicts which now may be analysed as a tale of romantic sublimation that led him to a secret marriage in order to escape the auto-erotic or homosexual pressures of a monastic life for himself. Discovering the marriage, Fulbert fumed and ordered his men to mutilate Abélard, which they did to such an extent that he was compelled to leave Héloïse despite her passionate love for him. Abélard then entered the Benedictine order and Héloïse retired to a convent. This did not mean that our once virile hero assumed the role of an impotent male in the herd, though such a change in his personality has been implied.[4] Abélard continued to battle and gained a measure of self-respect and praise from his opponents. Never would he be intimidated; nor would he be made petulant, weak or crooked. When he lost, he lost cleanly and honestly; and because he refused to be vanquished, he came to be more highly regarded and accepted.

Seeking a compensatory outlet in theology, Abélard joined Anselm of Laon, only to have this association bring out the same pattern of insubordination as in the past. Intolerant of restraint, totally devoid of respect for authority and fond of exhibiting his extraordinary talents, he fought with Anselm and preferred victory to truth. In retrospect, Abélard displayed a personality trait disturbance, aggressive type. His behaviour was characterized by a, more or less, constant irritation to frustration and a marked feeling of resentment with a 'chip on the shoulder' attitude.[5] His enemies charged him with heresy eventually and summoned him before the council of Soissons, which ordered him to recite the Athanasian Creed and burn his book on the Trinity.

Some years later, Abélard recovered and resumed his lectures and soon attracted large numbers of students; but, once again, his nose for trouble showed as he rankled the monks and they reported him to the Vatican. He appealed to the Church authorities and received permission to accept the hospitality of Cluny, where he spent the last two years of his life in relative peace. Abélard, the perpetuator of the Carolingian Renaissance, died in Chalons-sur-Saone—four leagues distant from Cluny— and was buried at Paraclete. When Héloïse passed on, she shared the same tomb with her lover until the Revolution removed both to Père Lachaise in Paris, where they now rest.[6]

While Abélard lived, French deeds were illustrated beautifully in the famed *chansons de geste*. Then the spirit of nationalism ignited and burned evenly until its volcanic eruption with the storming of the Bastille. After Abélard died, an inexhaustible stream of stories began to flow; countless dialogues, allegoric dramas, lyric poems and mysteries known as *fabliaux* demonstrated unique talent for projecting feelings into fiction. These didactic, entertaining works became bottomless springs for the ever-thirsty minds of Rabelais, Chaucer, Boccaccio and Goethe, and thus contributed ever so slightly to the mental health notions of the future.

This may be termed a period of oral, sublime gratification, which embraced an entire nation; for everything, routine chores, art, religion and science, was expressed in verse as a most delectable pastime. Even encyclopedic works and moral theses that were written in octosyllable thrilled readers until the era of uninhibited romance and song yielded to the ballad, the rondeau and the triolet with their rigid rules and refined structure.

BARTHOLOMEW

One source of evidence, and it is very strikingly complete, that the insane were treated well during this period is to be found in a small manual compiled by Bartholomew the Englishman, who was a Franciscan friar. Known by his Latin name of *Bartholomaeus Anglicus*, he gathered together an immense amount of information and designed his text particularly for priests. In it, Bartholomew dealt with a great many practical questions that could be used to furnish instruction to parishioners. He intended it to be a handbook, a work of reference in which answers might be located easily. The fact that a large number of manuscript copies were available stamped it as one of the most popular works of the Middle Ages. Before the invention of printing, Bartholomew's manual had been translated into five modern languages; and it continued to be used for several hundred years! The book was first written in Latin because, as the language of the Catholic Church, most priests could then consult it readily, but manifestly it came to be read also by the laity, as is evident from the translations. Jean Corbichon, an Augustinian, made a French translation which, itself, is a literary monument. John de Trevisa translated it into English. There are other translations into Italian, Spanish and Provençal.

After the invention of the printing press, Bartholomew's book, the title of which is *De Proprietatibus Rerum* (*The Properties of Things*), was published in a number of editions, no less than three times as an *incunabulum*—that is, before 1501—and more than twelve times later. Obviously in great demand, the book reached the hands of practically all of the clerics; at least all of those who could then read.

What Bartholomew said with regard to insanity, in general, represented the opinion of the churchmen of his time better than could be obtained from any other reference. His book was actually used as a text in the schools of theology, and may be quoted confidently as constituting the source of knowledge on all these dubious questions. What Bartholomew wrote with regard to causes, symptoms and treatments may be condensed into a single brief paragraph[7]:

Bartholomew listed the psychological causes of insanity as passion, overwork, too deep thought, sorrow, intensive study and fear. He then outlined physical factors which may disturb mentality: 'Insanity may come as the result of an infection, from the bite of a mad dog or some other venomous animal'. Insanity may also be related to overeating and overdrinking of strong wine. Bartholomew pointed out that not all patients suffer in

Rhazes

Averroes

Rake's Progress

the same way. He described two forms of mania as excitement and melancholia. Bartholomew also warned that some insane may hurt themselves or others, and for this reason these patients must be restrained. In so far as treatment, he recommended a change of environment to renew their health and strength. They must also be removed from the source of their agitation. Music should be provided for their recreation and suitable occupation should be planned for them.

These instructions about mental illness have been considered among the best brief formulas on the subject. Few, if any, contemporary writers have given as practical a notion of the whole concept of insanity as was actually presented by Bartholomew, the medieval friar whose influence, more than that of any other person, remained alive for so long after his death. Unfortunately, however, the development of the witchcraft delusion and the decadence of hospitals following the Reformation brought about the serious neglect of the insane and popularized the idea of possession by evil spirits. It has been observed that the Catholic countries were ever so much less affected by the witchcraft delusion than the reformed countries, and the deterioration of hospitals was not nearly too marked in them. Italy and Spain are examples of two countries where hospitals went on to provide better care for the insane than in those which had been disturbed by the religious conflicts.

In Bartholomew's day, the insane were accepted as sick people and placed in general hospitals to be treated. But sadly this concept was washed away in the devastating flood of time. In our own day, the insane have been rejected as irresponsible people and dumped into huge institutions to be isolated. The operation of this rejection mechanism is related to the fact that the mentally ill lack appeal. They do not recognize their illness; they do not want help; they do not evoke sympathy. Like the sociopath, they, too, often express hostility that generates hostility in others and hampers treatment. Yet how else can those react who, because of their condition, must be forcibly removed from the community, detained and imprisoned? Add to this several hundred units of electro-shock 'therapy' and little wonder the patients' disability is reinforced. By then they are convinced that everyone is against them. Clifford W. Beers tried to shed some light on this problem when he said: 'Madmen are too often man-made'.

It should be added that patients who need early treatment and never receive it tend to develop more severe symptoms. Increased opportunity for voluntary admission and less stigma are necessary to reduce resistance to treatment. If patients in the incipient stage of their illness remove themselves from an anxiety-producing environment and enter one which affords rest, medication, an orderly routine, interesting activities, wholesome food, they frequently proceed to improve. This was the sort of treatment that psychiatric patients received as far back as the middle of the thirteenth century.

BEDLAM BEGGARS

Even at this early date, as the population increased there was a corresponding increase in mental illness which, in turn, led to the formation of special institutions. For instance, the priory of St Mary of Bethlehem was designed in 1247 by Simon FitzMary, Sheriff of London, as a general hospital for the poor, but in 1403 it began to admit the insane and soon 'softened' its name to Old Bedlam.

From a formal historical view, early Bedlam had one noteworthy feature for the care of the insane in that it had sort of an 'open door programme'. More often than not, Bedlam granted 'trial visits' for patients when they improved spontaneously, and out of this system evolved an unusual method of obtaining sympathetic treatment from the citizens. Recovered patients wore special badges that identified them as former residents of Bedlam who were now privileged to return to the outside. Such a policy practically made the community responsible for the patients once they left the hospital.

When Christian charity failed to motivate the citizens to treat the insane kindly, then fear that they might become violent kept many from disturbing them. Because of this, the favourable public treatment of the Bedlamers, or Bedlamites, encouraged 'sturdy vagrants', *validi vagrantes*, to beg, borrow or steal the badge in order to secure the privileges that would be accorded them while they wore it.

Throughout the years there have been a number of references to these 'Bedlam beggars', who wandered about the English countryside and acquired the name Tom o' Bedlam. Others carried the more obscure title of Abram Man, so-called from the Abraham ward in Bedlam, whose inmates decorated themselves 'with party-coloured ribbons, tape in their hats, a fox-tail hanging down, a long stick with streamers' to beg alms. Under cover of this innocuous disguise, the Abram Men, a set of rugged rogues, shammed lunacy and had wit enough to steal as they went along. Their female counterpart and vagrant went by the title Bess o' Bedlam.

Many of the beggars adapted ever so quickly to the role which became increasingly profitable for them; they composed mad songs and no doubt made variations on their favourite theme. None had the crazy force and excitement of the original: its daring imagery, its wild language; its eloquence could have only been written by a gifted poet. Some have suspected that the author was William Shakespeare himself:[8]

> From the hag and hungry goblin
> That into rags would rend ye,
> All the spirits that stand
>   By the naked man
> In the book of moons, defend ye,
> That of your five sound senses
> You never be forsaken,
>   Nor wander from
>   Yourselves with Tom
> Abroad to beg your bacon.

Bedlam eventually became the byword for cruelty and a place where patients were exhibited like animals in a zoo to amuse the public. Although it prevailed in England, this inhuman practice was common elsewhere, and especially so in the Lunatics' Tower or *Narrentürme* of Vienna. Some idea of how the insane were treated may be seen from an inventory of supplies made in 1399 which listed: 'eleven chains of iron, two pairs of stocks, six locks and keys and four sets of manacles'.[9]

William Hogarth, a master pictorial satirist, depicted quite vividly the abominable conditions at Bedlam in one of the series of *The Rake's Progress*: the Rake is portrayed in the foreground while to the one side 'there are two visitors—a fashionable lady and her maid—in the gallery. . . . Strolling up and down, as people did at the time. Amidst the ruins of modesty and decency the lady only permits herself to leer through the sticks of her fan at something that we cannot see: Less hypocritical or not so refined, the lady's maid gazes and describes'—denuded human beings, covered with their own excreta, undernourished and literally rotting in body and mind. This shameful policy of displaying the insane did not end until 1751 at St Luke Hospital, London; and about twenty years later, Bedlam made a feeble move in the same direction when it specified that visitors would be admitted by ticket only and must view the patients in the presence of attendants.[10]

In 1815, a Committee of the House of Commons exposed the disgraceful conditions at Bedlam. That year another asylum was erected at St George's Fields, Lambeth; but, strangely, it was excluded from the official inspections which the Lord Ashley Act (1845) finally legalized for such institutions. And when a government survey (1851) revealed the sad state of affairs, reforms were introduced and the asylums were placed under the authority of the Lunacy Commissioners. Since then, Bedlam could be correctly called Bethlem Royal Hospital. Before then, it was no more of an acceptable hospital than a fox-hole on a battlefield is an adequate shelter.

On another mental health front, medieval Europe had its share of monastic functionaries who were anonymous, faceless and formless when it came to worldly problems. They seldom made contact with outsiders. They hardly ever talked with anyone personally; and, even in meetings of two or three of their own, they spoke in the murky cadences of a dialectical robot, lest they be understood. They prayed, they worked. Or to put it bluntly, if any one of them tried to live—say suspended between heaven and earth—he would be counselled out of the order and sent back home in a hurry.

Yet in an age of this socially approved group-schizophrenia, some men, however few, bore no resemblance to their medieval brethren. Bartholomew was one of these men and he flourished in the mid-thirteenth century. We have seen what strides he made on the practical side of mental health. There were others, too, but their contributions were mainly on the theoretical and on the literary plane.

These were men who loved to know what was astir in the world—and what was about to be stirred up next. These were men who rolled back the frontier of ignorance and superstition; who were responsible for clearing the channels of communication; who were capable of reducing the art of obfuscation to monosyllabic proportions. These were men who directed institutes of philosophy where young students could learn to harness undisciplined minds; who taught that cultures provided some purpose for human activity higher than mere survival; who led scholars into storehouses of knowledge; who certified students as qualified to identify with the intellectuals of their time. These were men who in their unique way offered new hope for all. These were men who were well represented in their time by Roger Bacon and Thomas Aquinas.

ROGER BACON

Roger Bacon is important to mental health in that he persevered along a truly scientific course. In spite of some stumbling into theologic pitfalls, he regained his posture to stand as one of the great masters in the evolution of human thought. The value of the scientific method to individual mental health and creative problem-solving needs no elaboration. When viewed against the cultural background in which he lived, the contribution of Bacon is even more remarkable. It was an age in which science introduced the objective *method* to an unready society. It was an age that could no more accept the *method* of science than the *results* of science. It was an age that was trapped by time—time required to grow above and beyond a superstitious past. It was an age that was deeply absorbed in theological and philosophical speculations and still managed to move ahead, if at an agonizingly creeping pace.[11]

Ironically however, the personal mental health of Bacon failed to sway contemporary thinking. He had a marked affinity for controversy, as was evident in his fanatical attempt to reform medieval society by insisting on the use of experimentation and acidly condemning deduction in an age that thrilled at the prospects of dealing with metaphysical problems. Part of his trouble also stemmed from his firebrand temperament which spared no words and no one. He assailed Alexander of Hales, the *Irrefragable Doctor*, saying that his *Summa* was '*plus quam pondus unius equi?*' He spoke disparingly of Albert the Great, calling him ignorant and presumptuous, and he expressed contempt for Aquinas and his ideas. He attacked the bishops, the medicant orders and the papal court. Paradoxically, Bacon discredited those who worked for a cause that he himself was otherwise so well fitted to defend.

Some of the situations against which Bacon inveighed were real abuses. He complained of certain procedures in education; he urged a return to Hippocrates and Aristotle in that mental diseases were *natural* and not *supernatural* disorders. The fact that his criticisms were sound was far outweighed by the imprudent manner in which he presented them; and, consequently, many turned upon him. Greatest of all his enemies was Bonaventura, the theologic idol of that period, the *Seraphic Doctor*, the General of the Franciscan order in which Bacon had taken vows. Thus, as Bacon's superior, in 1257 Bonaventura forbade the troublesome monk to lecture, ordered him to Paris and kept him under close surveillance.

This, however, was just the beginning of Bacon's difficulties. He had to meet another charge, the charge of Satanic intervention in science; hence he faced that goodly missile which with the epithets 'infidel' and 'atheist' has settled the fate of so many battles. . . . In defence, Bacon selected a most unfortunate weapon, a weapon which hurt him more than the enemy, for he argued against the idea of compacts with Satan, and showed that much ascribed to demons results from natural means. Such comments only added oil to the fire, for limiting the power of Satan was hardly less impious than limiting the power of God.

Even his friend, Guy of Foulques, who became Pope Clement IV in 1265, could protect him but a short time before the mounting fury of his enemies. As Bacon prepared to perform a few experiments to demonstrate his theories to a small group, all Oxford rose against him. It seemed that hell was about to break loose. Priests, monks, fellows and students rushed about, their garments streaming in the wind, and everywhere rose the cry, 'Down with the magician!' and this cry, 'Down with the magician!' resounded from cell to cell and hall to hall.

Jerome de Ascoli, the General of the Franciscan order in 1278, decided that Roger was too dangerous to be at large and ordered him restricted to the monastery, and there Bacon remained confined for fourteen years! How deeply the struggle had racked his mind may be gleaned from one of his last remarks: 'Would that I had not given myself so much trouble for the love of science'.

When W. R. Newbold deciphered the Voynich manuscript, he reported that Bacon was far ahead of his time, that he probably should be credited with the invention of gunpowder, the microscope, the telescope and eyeglasses. Human cells, seminiferous tubules and spermatozoa may also have been known to him. He even predicted that wagons minus horses and ships without sails would move with incredible speed. Moreover, he believed that man would learn to travel by air. But Bacon was compelled to write in an obscure language, for him to question the Biblical views of physical science would have been indeed perilous. About 1663, John Dryden summed up his works in these lines:

> The World to Bacon does not only owe
> Its present Knowledge, but its future too.

THOMAS AQUINAS

Thomas Aquinas also directed his abundant energy and talent toward the cause of mental health. When it came to the sick of mind, his primary interest focused on canon law. This involved a legal approach that emphasized varieties in degree of insanity rather than varieties in kind (types and nature) which is a medico-psychological issue. Aquinas concerned himself with the degree of incapacity engendered by the disorder. The Angelic Doctor illustrated this point well in his *Summa*, where he reinforced the custom of the Catholic Church to baptize the mentally ill and feebleminded in the following categories: (1) those insane from infancy without any lucid intervals; (2) those enjoying periods of lucidity, even though insane from infancy; (3) those who have at one time been sane but have suffered the loss of reason; (4) those who are mentally deficient but can, nevertheless, take thought for their salvation and are, in some way at least, capable of appreciating the sacraments.

On the subject of suicide, however, Aquinas simply echoed the Church's severe attitude when he wrote: 'It is the most fatal of sins, because it cannot be repented of'. In respect to marriage he repeated in explicit terms the doctrine of the incapacity of the insane to make a valid contract. And with one brief paragraph, Aquinas summarized this question:

'I *answer* that Insanity is either previous or subsequent to marriage. If subsequent, it nowise voids the marriage, but if it be previous, then the insane person either has lucid periods, or not. If he has, then, although it is not safe for him to marry during that lucid interval, since he would not know how to educate his children, yet if he marries, the marriage is valid. But if he has no lucid intervals, or marries outside them, then since there can be no consent without the use of reason, the marriage will be invalid.'

John Duns Scotus opposed the views of Aquinas and emphatically linked mental disorders with Satan. The uncompromising Scotus and his hair-splitting Dunsers prompted William Tyndale to remark: 'The old barking curs raged in every pulpit'. Their cavilling resistance to progress in learning lead to the word *dunce* and moved Samuel Butler to pen these lines in *Hudibras*:

> He knew what's what, and that's as high
> As metaphysic wit can fly . . .
> A second Thomas, or at once
> To name them all, another Dunse.

The breach in philosophy grew ever wider with the likes of William Durandus, a man of little learning and shallow understanding. He was followed by William of Ockham, a sceptic by implication whose concepts were alive with the ghosts of Neo-Platonism. Because these and other philosophers failed to grasp the objective spirit of Aristotle and Aquinas, circular arguments and fruitless discussions prevailed which, in turn, antagonized generations of scientists, so that the schism between philosophy and mental science seemed irreparable, a break that accelerated the decline of medieval wisdom.[12]

Arnold of Villanova, alchemist, astrologer, physician, reflected the growing nebulous attitude toward mental illness in the same century that Aquinas lived. He is mentioned here because of his acceptance of the Galenic principle of organicity while, at the same time, believing in the devil and astrology. At first, Arnold attempted to reconcile the humoralism of Galen with demonism by claiming that if certain warm humours developed in the body, the devil, and particularly the incubi, might seize the victim because the devil likes warmth.

Then, Galen's theories had to be brought into the orbit of astrology; so Arnold said that epilepsy was caused by the phlegm if it appeared at the same time as the first quarter of the moon. He localized it in the blood if it occurred in the second and third quarters; in blackbile if in the last. Melancholia was due to Mars: the colour and heat of the bile had something to do with the colour and heat of the planet. Arnold recommended bleeding, but he instructed that the phases of the moon and the constellations must be watched. He considered the sign of the Cancer most favourable for bloodletting. His version of the famous Salernitan poem, *Flos Medicine*, served as the backbone of applied psychotherapy up to the time of the Renaissance. It was memorized by innumerable physicians for whom each of its verses had the quality of the Holy Writ. The seductive features of the poem's lines spread simple maxims throughout the world:

> The spring is moist of temper good and warme,
> Then best it is to bathe, to sweate, and purge,
> Then may one ope a veine in either arme,
> If boyling bloud or fears of agues urge:
> Then Venus recreation doth no harme,
> Yet may too much thereof turne to a scourge.

Plainly, the application of sadistic practices extended far beyond the mental healing arts. It entered into the temper and texture of medieval thinking and ideology. When Arnold was a young man, penitential cults of flagellants originated in Perugia, Italy (1260), who believed they could expiate their evils by self-punishment. Members of these fanatical societies marched in grotesque public processions and scourged one another with cords and whips until blood squirted from their bodies. For them such self-inflicted mortification absolved guilt and exorcised disease-bearing demons; consequently, the flagellants doubted the needs for sacraments and questioned the value of medicine. In view of the heresy and excesses, the flagellant movement was condemned severely by the Catholic Church; but before it faded away, the barbaric custom flared up again and again in various parts of the world.

While the bubonic plague ravaged country after country, the scourging cult spread to ordinary people who, instead of whipping themselves, displaced their macabre aggression upon the

Jews, whom they accused of black magic and of poisoning the wells to bring on the plague. Throughout Europe, large groups of Jews were sacrificed as scapegoats simply because they had no effective means of retaliation. In Mainz, twelve thousand hurled themselves into a flaming holocaust prepared for their execution. And modern-day demonstrations against minority groups have sadly shown that this dastardly display of mass sociopathic behaviour was not an exclusive birthright of the Middle Ages.

Another tragic event, indirectly related to mental health, occurred at Toulouse (1275), the hot-bed of Catharan infection, where the earliest execution of a witch took place. In this case, the victim 'confessed' that she bore a monster after intercourse with the devil. She told of nourishing the creature with babies' flesh which she obtained on her nocturnal journeys. Little did anyone realize then that such fantastic beliefs would snowball within two centuries and reach the most unimaginable proportions.

BIBLIOGRAPHY

1. Gregory Zilboorg, *A History of Medical Psychology*, Allen & Unwin, London, 1941, p. 116.
2. Arturo Castiglioni, *A History of Medicine*, Knopf, New York, 1947, p. 319.
3. R. Colin Pickett, *Mental Affliction and Church Law*, University of Ottawa, Ottawa, 1952, p. 27.
4. Alexis Carrel, *Man the Unknown*, Harper & Brothers, New York, 1935, p. 143.
5. Thomas F. Graham, *Dynamic Psychopathology*, Christopher, Boston, 1957, p. 177.
6. William Turner, *History of Philosophy*, Ginn, Boston, 1903, p. 285.
7. James J. Walsh, *The History of Nursing*, Kenedy, New York, 1929, p. 103.
8. Louis Untermeyer, *A Treasury of Great Poems*, Simon & Schuster, New York, 1942, p. 172.
9. E. G. O'Donoghue, *The Story of Bethlehem Hospital*, Unwin, London, 1914, p. 69.

10. Lucy R. Seymer, *A General History of Nursing*, Macmillan, New York, 1949, p. 232.
11. Andrew D. White, *A History of the Warfare of Science with Theology*, Appleton, New York, 1896, p. 386.
12. Robert E. Brennan, *History of Psychology*, Macmillan, New York, 1945, p. 80.

CHAPTER FOUR

KRAMER TO LUTHER

The sad state of affairs in mental health of the late fifteenth century was reflected in the attitude of the otherwise humane and scholarly Johannes Tritheim, a Benedictine abbot, who wanted more Inquisitors to deal with witches: 'Man and beast die as a result of the evil of these women. . . . Many suffer constantly from the most severe diseases and are not even aware that they are bewitched.' He lived at a time that not only terrified the people with tales of witch-hunting but also plunged Europe into fierce religious strife; lowered literature into the medium of denominational controversy; abhorred art as the handmaiden of Satanism; choked medicine with a swelling wave of superstition; abolished academic freedom; blocked experimentation; burned books and stymied mental health progress at almost every turn.

HAMMER OF WITCHES

Not long after the invention of printing, the *Malleus Maleficarum* or *Hammer of Witches* rolled off the presses. The day it appeared was indeed a dark one for all of mankind, since the text soon become the handbook of the Inquisition and the 'operational manual' of psychopathology. Written by two extremely methodical Dominicans, Henry Kramer and James Sprenger, the manuscript received the endorsement of Pope Innocent and King Maximilian. Thereby armed with the power of the Holy See and Royal Throne, the compulsive authors approached the Faculty of Theology at the University of Cologne and 'persuaded' the reluctant professors to add their approval; and when they did, their Letter of Approbation opened with these words:[1]

'In the name of our Lord Jesus Christ, Amen. Know all men by these presents, whosoever shall read, see or hear the tenor of this official and public document, that in the year of our Lord, 1487, upon a Saturday, being the nineteenth day of the month of May, at the fifth hour after noon, or thereabouts, in the third year of the Pontificate of our most Holy Father and Lord, the lord Innocent, by divine providence Pope, the eighth of that name, in the very and actual presence of me Arnold Kolich, public notary, and in the presence of the witnesses whose names are hereunder written and who were convened and especially summoned for this purpose, the Venerable and Very Reverend Father Henry Kramer, Professor of Sacred Theology, of the Order of Preachers, Inquisitor of heretical depravity, directly delegated thereto by the Holy See together with the Venerable and Very Reverend Father James Sprenger, Professor of Sacred Theology and Prior of the Dominican Convent at Cologne, being especially appointed as colleague of the said Father Henry Kramer, hath on behalf both of himself and his said colleague made known unto us and declared that the Supreme Pontiff now happily reigning, lord Innocent, Pope, as hath been set out above, hath committed and granted by a bull duly signed and sealed unto the aforesaid Inquisitors Henry and James, members of the Order of Preachers and Professors of Sacred Theology, by His Supreme Apostolic Authority, the power of making search and inquiry into all heresies, and most especially into the heresy of witches, an abomination that thrives and waxes strong in these our unhappy days, and he has bidden them diligently to perform this duty throughout the five Archdioceses of the five Metropolitan Churches, that is to say, Mainz, Cologne, Treves, Salzburg and Bremen, granting them every faculty of judging and proceeding against such even with the power of putting malefactors to death, according to the tenor of the Apostolic bull, which they hold and possess and have exhibited unto us, a document which is whole, entire, untouched, and in no way lacerated or impaired, in fine whose integrity is above any suspicion. And the tenor of the said bull commences thus: "Innocent, Bishop, Servant of the servants of God, for an eternal remembrance. Desiring with the most heartfelt anxiety, even as Our Apostleship requires, that the Catholic Faith should especially in this Our day increase and flourish everywhere, ... "and it concludes thus: "Given at Rome, at S. Peter's, on the 9 December of the Year of the Incarnation of Our Lord one thousand, four hundred and eighty-four, in the first Year of Our Pontificate".'

Thus, the most horrible document of its age brushed aside all of the data that had been gathered so painstakingly about mental ills through past centuries and, in short, with a pious-sounding rationalization accused countless psychotics of witchcraft. Undoubtedly it was a kind of 'persecutory mania' manifested by the Catholic Church and German State as a means of containing any challenge to their authority and security. For years it rated as the chief text of anti-Satanism in Europe.

Divided into three parts, the book first dealt with the 'three necessary concomitants of witchcraft, that is, the devil, a witch and permission of Almighty God'. From a Biblical frame of reference, it tried to prove in eighteen questions that non-believers in witchcraft were either heretics or sincerely mistaken. Next came 'treating of the methods by which the works of witchcraft are wrought and directed and how they may be successfully annulled and dissolved'. Here but two questions were 'resolved' in eight chapters. This section discussed the nature of witchcraft, its satanic horrors and the manner of treatment. Kind of a clinical approach: diagnosis and therapy? The third part related to the 'judicial proceedings in both the ecclesiastical and civil courts against witches and indeed all heretics'. Sort of legal-like: objective and just? Yet if the defendant admitted seeing the devil, this hallucination was accepted as valid—no need for a *corpus delicti*!

A misogyny from cover to cover, the text showed notable animus against females. Never since the fall of Eve were women so degraded. Once labelled a witch, a woman was not permitted to face her mad tormentors. They ripped off her clothing, shaved her head and pubes so that no demons could hide anywhere on her body; and thus exposed, she was led to the court backwards so that her eyes would not cast an evil spell upon the judge. Despite its cruel and unsavoury details, the book revealed some insights into the forces which operated then as an outgrowth of contemporary unrest.

In an age of the most rigid self-denial, the *Hammer of Witches* pounded away at all forms of human behaviour, especially erotic. With a righteous serenity, it told how Lucifer and his cohorts could injure humanity:[2]

'And one is, to induce an evil love in a man for a woman, or in a woman for a man. The second is to plant hatred or jealousy in anyone. The third is to bewitch them so that a man cannot perform the genital act with a woman, or conversely a woman with a man; or by various means to procure an abortion, as had been said before. The fourth is to cause some disease in any of the human organs. The fifth, to take away life. The sixth, to deprive them of reason.'

Painters also splashed on canvas the wild imaginations of the time in which they lived. Except for slight variations in certain instances, many art works depicted devils as real beings who attacked the bodies and minds of people. Two outstanding names, Hieronymus Bosch and Pieter Brueghel, synthesized the fantastic beliefs of their day. The famous *Temptation of St Antony* by Bosch is a pictorial counterpart of the *Malleus*, wherein Antony, seeking solitude in a ruined fortress, experiences episodes of the witches' sabbath, flights through the air, conferences of Satanists on the lake's edge, the black mass, devil pact and so on. In like manner, *The Last Judgment* represents gruesome elements from the *Apocalypse*, where the earth becomes a chaotic jumble, taken over by demons; flaming towns reflect a background of horror in the sky; hell breaks loose everywhere: here a man burned alive, there hanged, there quartered, there throttled. The millstone, the water torture and the wheel pile on agony. A devil glides around on the back of a

artin Luther by Cranach

itzwilliam Museum, Cambridge)

Henricus Cornelius
Agrippa.
Eques, Medicinæ et Juris
utriusque Doctor.

Heinrich Agrippa

witch, moaning lemures; infernal monsters charge a terrified humanity.

More of the same morbidity came from the brush of Brueghel. His *Fall of the Rebel Angels* and *Dulle Griet* illustrate one macabre scene after another. In the first painting, the spectre of a nightmare faun and creatures with mollusc bodies and bat wings symbolize the casting of the damned from the heights of heaven to the depths of hell. Like the *Triumph of Death*, the *Dulle Griet* portrays an armed amazon sweeping across hell with ghoulish scenes all about: here an executioner, there a gallows and strewn everywhere is the havoc of a relentless mower. The background includes plague-victims, groups locked in a battle and a shipwreck on the horizon.[3]

Again, labouriously produced block-books like *La Danse Macabre* (*Dance of Death*) and the *Ars Moriendi* may be related to the iconography of Bosch and Breughel. These xylographic booklets also illustrate the obsessions of their time with psychomachia—an everlasting conflict between Good and Evil for human souls. The familiar and quaint figures of *La Danse Macabre* inspired Goethe to tell their story in verse, and his poem prompted Camille Saint-Saëns, the French pianist, to give it a symphonic setting:[4]

> The Warden looks down at the mid hour of night
> On the tombs that lie scattered below;
> The moon fills the place with her silvery light,
> And the churchyard like day seems to glow.
> When see! First one grave, then another, opes wide,
> And women and men stepping forth are descried
> In garments snow white and trailing.
> . . . And a rattle and clatter soon rises high
> As of one beating time to the dance.

In its naïve symbolism, the *Ars Moriendi* of Antonio Verard represents the sheerest terror that one faces in the final hour. These images depict a celestial tug-of-war of howling demons pulling against haloed angels for the soul of a dying person. One false idea, one errant move, is all that is needed to betray him. The devils induce despair by showing him the man he killed, his adulterous mistress and the goods he stole. And if the vicious band of incubi lost the soul to heaven, they flapped away on their bat-wings to besiege another death-bed.

BIRTH OF A REFORMER

Martin Luther was a growing boy when much of this took place. Born in 1483, he moved clearly into our mental health story at the age of twenty-six. It was then that he discovered the Pauline doctrine of salvation by personal faith which led him to challenge the Church doctrine of salvation by prescriptive works. Let us go back to that period and let us try to understand what happened to Luther at that psychological moment:[5]

'. . . He continued a diligent study of the Bible, and one day as he was reading in the tower of the Augustinian convent where he lived, he came upon a short sentence in the Epistle to the Romans, *"The just shall live by faith"*. Now for Brother Martin was the world made over. In deep and constant meditation, he came finally to see that the Bible teaching was different from the theology which he had been taught. *It was not by man's work, but by his faith, that he was saved.* An extraordinary peace came to abide in his soul. It seemed to him that now at last he was a Christian, a good Catholic. Here was the foundation stone of religion.'

For Luther, the tower incident meant true conversion and psychological freedom. For him, it represented justification by faith rather than by works. It also gave him the weapon of personal conviction which he used so courageously to undercut the shameless traffic in indulgencies. But the manner in which he carried out his reforms was no less misleading than the one which he tried to eliminate.

According to Johann Goethe, the tragedy of Luther's crusade was that it set back intellectual progress by appealing to the emotions of the masses. The poet believed that abstract theological questions should have been handled by calm, neutral scholars who were able to couch the difficult Christian concepts in terms simple enough to be understood by most of the people. Had this taken place, then the hatreds, the conflicts and the persecutions might not have been so intense nor so prolonged.

F. Somner Merryweather, a Protestant author, deplored the destruction of the medieval libraries which was triggered by the fanaticism of Luther and his followers. This delightful booklover sighed with mournful regret over the sad deeds of those men who carried out the Reformation:[6]

'. . . the careless grants of a licentious monarch conferred a monastery on a court favourite or political partizan, without one thought for the preservation of its contents . . . less learned hands had rifled those parchment collections long ago, mutilated their finest volumes by cutting out with childish pleasure the illuminations with which they were adorned; tearing off the bindings for the gold clasps which protected the treasures within, and chopping up huge folios as fuel for their blazing hearths, and immense collections were sold as waste paper.' John Bale also lamented the loss of the monks' books, even though he was one of their bitterest foes.

Desiderius Erasmus, the timid intellectual, turned into a verbal bear when he could no longer tolerate the disorder about him: '*Ubicumque regnat Lutheranismus, ibi literarum est interitus*', 'Wherever Lutherism reigns, there literature utterly perishes'. The scholar of Rotterdam added: 'I dislike these Gospellers on many accounts, but chiefly because through their agency, literature languishes, disappears, lies drooping and perishes; and without learning, what is man's life? They love good cheer and a wife; for other things they care not a straw.'

True or false, one thing certain, the first disciples of Luther went all out with chimerical and ruthless efforts to bury scholastic principles which for them symbolized authority, ecclesiasticism and orthodoxy. Condemning the past as 'rigid and static', these capricious reformers extolled their own ideas as modern inspirations from on high. Then ancestral standards and values became so thoroughly embalmed with disdain and scorn to eradicate any residual signs of unity. Mental health reached its lowest point when schools of mysticism evolved from the theological tenets of this period and carried the trademark of a psychological dualism which underscored the antithesis of body and mind.

A perusal of Luther's Latin works reveals them to be coarse, nimious, inelegant, scurrilous and as redundant as these adjectives which describe them. Their wild paradoxes, their overgeneralizations, their incredible conclusions menace the very foundation of religious morality. They are neither compensated, nor strong, much less eloquent. His letter to Erasmus, prefixed to the article *De Servo Arbitrio*, is replete with the most insolent terms. Any comprehensive line of argument that would clarify Luther's ideas is sadly missing. Throughout his writings an unchecked dogmatism rests on an absolute confidence in the practical infallibility of his own judgment. He allows no pause, shows no concern for the hesitant; whatever stands before him, the Church, the canons, the councils, the scholars, are all swept away in a stream of impetuous declamation; and since any part of the Bible, as Luther saw it, is easily understood, and only understood, in his sense, any deviation from his doctrine is subject to the anathema of perdition.

ANALYSIS OF LUTHER

What about the mental health of the most controversial figure of his time? Did he suffer a personality disorder? Such a suspicion first appeared years ago when a medical anthropologist wrote:[7]

'These prophets and seers have left an impression that shall last so long as theology itself endures, yet the visions of epileptic Mahomet, of Bunyan and Martin Luther were the flickerings of insanity, albeit called the sacred fire of holy inspiration.' And then Ernst Kretschmer, a German alienist, described the behaviour of the fiery reformer in this manner:[8]

'Luther had severe, and to a certain extent endogenous, emotional disturbances, and certain attacks of melancholia of a definitely pathological nature, with striking bodily symptoms accompanying them. . . .' He represented a type of homely hero, a wholehogger, a fighter with melancholic and schizothymic characteristics. A man of pronounced cyclothymic-hypomanic traits, Luther displayed a 'tendency to congenital emotional disturbances'. Kretschmer then mentioned Luther's pyknic physique and 'explained' his 'well-defined schizothymic streaks by the portraits and characterology of his parents', and pictures of himself, as a youth, which showed a tendency to angular profile. These heterogeneous qualities condition the tenacity of will and fanaticism.

Such a type lacks flexible, conciliatory quality and talent for organization. The greatness of men like Luther lies in a blazing, explosive nature, which—'in real hypomanic fashion'—sets aflame at the first rush, tears down, tugs forward and sweeps together everything in its way, leaving the rebuilding for others. The emotional politics of the rotund Luther and the good-humoured obesity of the equally pyknic rulers who sided with him stamped the beginning of the German Reformation, in so far as organization or the lack of it, with a cyclothymic label. Luther was a man or inimitable homeliness, but the masses loved his puerile qualities, his direct, noble storminess, his boisterous passion and defiance, his moving, rough speech, his fidelity and his coarse-grained mother-wit.

Not all writers agreed with Kretschmer's evaluation. One biographer defended the Protestant leader with these words:[9] 'Yet Luther was at times severely depressed, and the reason lay not in any personal frictions but in the malaise of existence intensified by religion. . . . Neither can one blithely write off the case as an example of manic depression, since the patient exhibited a prodigious and continuous capacity for work of a high order.'

In a *Study in Psychoanalysis and History*, the raging but warmhearted Martin Luther is cast into an ambivalent role. On one side he appears as sort of an existential hero, an advocate of self-determination, parallel to Sigmund Freud and on the other, an upholder of power vested in a blind faith:[10]

'Luther tried to free individual conscience from totalitarian dogma; he meant to give man credal wholeness, and, alas, inadvertently helped to increase and to refine authoritarianism. Freud tried to free the individual's insight from authoritarian conscience; his wholeness is that of the individual ego, but the question is whether collective man will create a world worth being whole for. . . . Both men perfected introspective techniques permitting isolated man to recognize his individual patienthood. They also reasserted the other pole of existence, Man's involvement in generations; for only in facing the helplessness and the hope newly born in every child does mature man (and this *does* include woman) recognize the irrevocable responsibility of being alive and about.'

A man of many faces, the sixteenth-century Pope-baiter has also been compared to Blaise Pascal, John Bunyan, Jonathan Edwards, Soren Kierkegaard, Karl Marx, Fyodor Dostoevsky and Miguel Unamuno. Luther's philosophy was a projection of a conflict with his own father, and his character emanated from an anal-phallic basis associated with attacks on his behind: 'My mother caned me for stealing a nut, until the blood came. Such strict discipline drove me to the monastery, although she meant it well. My father once whipped me so that I ran away and felt ugly toward him until he was at pains to win me back. At school I was caned in a single morning fifteen times for nothing at all. I was required to decline and conjugate and hadn't learned my lessons.'

How little Luther understood the meaning of these early experiences is evident in his obsessive preoccupation with dirty infectious ideas wherein his booming oratory displaced nothing but flatulent expulsion. Random selections from the 6,596 entries of *Table Talk* projected material easily contained in an anal-erotic formula as noted by Luther's bluntness at a depressive moment when he thought of impending death: 'I am like ripe poop about to slip out of the world which is a gigantic rectum'. Sounds more like *Pooltable Talk* when one miscues with the nine-ball set up right in front of the side pocket. Cultured men regarded these invectives with outer alarm—and inner pleasure —but Roland H. Bainton explained that Luther attached himself to the mind of his age: 'Life itself stank, one could not walk around Wittenberg without encountering the odors of the pigsty, offal, and the slaughterhouse. And even the most genteel were not reticent about the facts of daily experience. Katie, when asked about the congregation on a day when Luther was unable to attend, replied: "The church was so full it stank". "Yes," said Luther, "they had manure on their boots."'

In so far as his oral habits, Luther not only imbibed but was rather proud of his capacity. He prized a drinking mug with three rings around it: the first represented the *Ten Commandments*, the second the *Apostle's Creed* and the third the *Lord's Prayer*. He thoroughly enjoyed telling how he often emptied the glass through the *Lord's Prayer*, whereas his friend, Johannes Agricola, could not pass the *Ten Commandments*. Yet Luther knew that the excessive use of alcohol weakened inhibitions:[11]

'It has been asked: Is an offence, committed in a moment of intoxication, therefore excusable? Most assuredly not; on the contrary, drunkenness aggravates the fault. Hidden sins unveil themselves when a man's self-possession goes from him; that which the sober man keeps in his breast, the drunken man lets out at the lips. Astute people, when they want to ascertain a man's true character, make him drunk. This same drunkness is a grievous vice among us Germans, and should be heavily chastised by the temporal magistrate, since the fear of God will not suffice to keep the brawling guzzlers in check.'

Needless to say, Luther made quite a clinical study. Many times, the blustering old beast substituted swearing for sublime prayer and rationalized his behaviour thus:[12] 'For I am unable to pray without at the same time cursing. If I am prompted to say, "Hallowed be thy name", I must add, "Cursed, damned, outraged be the name of papists". If I am prompted to say, "Thy Kingdom come", I must perforce add, "Cursed, damned destroyed must be the papacy".'

It may be concluded that these reactions expressed Luther's need for relief from inner pressure which threatened to make devotion intolerable for him—that is, just as he was about to reject God and himself. The regressive features of this stress and the subsequent obsessive and paranoid focus on the Pope and the Devil indicated that a transference with a theme of anal defiance had taken place from parental figures to scapegoats. Considering Luther's distress over giving to the Pope's fund, how would he have reacted to a psychoanalyst's fee of say $25.00 for a fifty-minute hour?

Victim of his own introspection, Luther wrote, in *Colloquia Mensalia*, how he threw ink pots and curses at the devil. He observed that Satan, a proud spirit, could not bear scorn or listen to holy names even if uttered in profanity. And if this failed, he said:

'Don't argue with the Devil. He has five thousand years of experience. . . . Seek company and discuss some irrelevant matter, as for example, what is going on in Venice. Shun solitude. Eve got into trouble when she walked in the garden alone. I have my worst temptations when I am by myself. Seek out some Christian brother, some wise counsellor. Undergird yourself with the fellowship of the church. Then, too, seek convivial company, feminine company, dine, dance, joke and sing. Make yourself eat and drink even though food may be very distasteful. Fasting is the very worst expedient.'

Once Luther gave three rules for dispelling despondency: The first is faith in Christ; the second is to get downright angry; and the third is the love of a woman. Music was especially commended. The devil hates it because he cannot endure gaiety. Incidentally, some Popish writers affirmed that Luther was begot by an incubus and strangled by Old Harry. Samuel Butler, with a shaft of irony, alluded to this aspersion:[13]

> Did not the devil appear to Martin
> Luther in Germany, for certain?
> And would have gull'd him with a trick,
> But Mart, was too too politic.

Formidable and stolid on the surface, Luther was actually a very defensive, a genuinely shy and a frightened individual. On December 4, 1521, he appeared on the streets of Wittenberg with a beard and hoped that he would not be easily recognized. As the days passed, his anxiety increased and he permitted the whiskers to get thick enough to deceive even his mother, for he knew that earlier there had been trouble when students and townsmen, armed with hidden knives, moved into a church, smashed the altar and intimidated the worshippers. But Luther was not involved, for he wanted no part of this mass psychology.

Many believed that the violence started as a 'mere squabble of monks', that is, between the Augustinian Luther and the Dominican John Tetzel. Then their differences were exploited by the German rulers and the political hacks who alleged that spiritual hawkers peddled indulgences which were compared to notes to be turned in at the gates of purgatory to allow a soul passage to Heaven. Meanwhile, the Dominicans rallied behind Tetzel who had been granted a doctorate so that he might be in a better position to publish counter-statements and to carry the fight to the reformers. Tetzel acknowledged the degree and roundly applauded the catching jingle:

> *Sobald der Pfennig im Kasten klingt,*
> *Die Seele aus dem Fegfeuer springt.*

> As soon as the coin in the coffer rings,
> The soul from purgatory springs.

At the peak of the controversy over indulgences, Luther lost his sense of logic and, anxious to implant the seed of the Reformation, appealed for the support of the princes, in a paper called *Argyrophilax*: 'You will find out how many hundred thousand gold pieces the monks and that class of men possess within a small portion of your territory'. Most likely, Luther was not aware of the pecuniary orientation of sixteenth-century capitalism as another effect of repressed anal pleasures, for soon the religious struggle coincided with a vast political and social revolution which spread crises throughout the Continent. It was a revolution from feudalism to monarchy, a violent period of change—hastened by the invention of gunpowder and the rise of nationalism. All of this divided European culture into separate cells and in doing so left an unsuitable environment for mental health which, like science and art, is ever involved in the process of internationalization.

In the wake of bloody battles which followed, Luther became terrified, and when he found that the greedy nobles cared no more for him and his married colleagues than for the celibate monks whose monasteries his revolt enabled them to plunder, he cried:[14] 'To the devil with senators, manor lords, princes and mighty nobles, who do not leave for the preachers, the services of the Gospel, wherewith to support their wives and children'.

Historians, be they psychological or be they political, recorded one of their darkest chapters. Monstrous evils of hate were aroused and brought forth. Religion challenged religion. Nation opposed nation. Brother fought brother. As a consequence, civilization was struck a most staggering blow. The underlying motives which perpetuated the disorder were summed up by Frederick the Great in a cynical apothegm: 'In Germany it was self-interest, in France the love of novelty, in England lust'.

BIBLIOGRAPHY

1. Montague Summers, Translator, *Malleus Maleficarum*, Rodker, London, 1928.
2. Montague Summers, *The History of Witchcraft and Demonology*, Kegan Paul, Trench, Trubner, London, 1926.
3. Emile Brouette, 'The Sixteenth Century and Satanism', *Satan*, Sheed and Ward, New York, 1951, pp. 310-348.
4. Hazel G. Kinscella, *Music and Romance*, Radio Corporation of America, Camden, 1941, p. 279.
5. Elsie Singmaster, *Martin Luther: the Story of His Life*, Houghton Mifflin, Boston, 1917, p. 33.
6. F. Somner Merryweather, *Bibliomania in the Middle Ages*, Merryweather, London, 1849, pp. 4-5.

7. G. Frank Lydston, *The Diseases of Society*, Lippincott, Philadelphia, 1904, p. 471.

8. W. J. H. Sprott, Translator, *Physique and Character*, Harcourt, Brace, New York, 1926, pp. 219-244.

9. Roland H. Bainton, *Here I Stand*, Abingdon-Cokesbury, New York, 1950, p. 23.

10. Erik H. Erikson, *Young Man Luther*, Norton, New York, 1958, p. 252.

11. William Hazlitt, Editor, *The Table Talk of Martin Luther*, Bell, London, 1890, p. 293.

12. William J. Durant, *The Reformation*, Simon and Schuster, New York, 1957, p. 418.

13. Samuel Butler, *Hudibras*, Warne, London, 1890, pp. 174 and 190.

14. Martin J. Spalding, *A History of the Protestant Reformation*, Murphy, Baltimore, 1860, p. 257.

CHAPTER FIVE

AGRIPPA TO BODIN

The fierce religious strife and the swelling wave of superstition combined in the sixteenth century to build a bastille of allegory and myth. Not even medicine with a long tradition of carrying the torch of enlightenment dared to challenge this fortress, for medicine was then a highly speculative branch of knowledge, containing features of alchemy, astrology, occultism and theology.

Three medical practitioners, however, refused to succumb to the spurious disciplines of antiquity. They were the rebels, the rebels with a cause, the rebels who sought passionately to roll back the frontier of the unknown, to remove the chains of ignorance, to halt the spread of terror. Against the stiffest kind of resistance from the Old Church, the *Malleus Maleficarum* and now the New Church, these rugged revolutionaries pressed ahead, ever mindful, ever undaunted of their heroic task, a task to lift man off the steaming floor of hell and bring him up to an atmosphere bearable for existence. Their names may be forgotten, but their deeds remain as lasting monuments to man's constant search for the truth.

HEINRICH AGRIPPA

Heinrich Agrippa, also known as Agrippa von Nettesheim, was born in Cologne, and because he came feet first and his mother suffered much pain during delivery they called him Agrippa—a Roman term that joined parts of the words for pain and foot. In a way, Agrippa explained that his name fits his temperament pretty well—for he entered many fights *aegris pedibus*. Recipient of a liberal education, he studied alchemy, astrology, medicine and philosophy. Destined for great things, Agrippa stood high among the first physicians who opposed the popular theory of demons while at the same time he argued that astral forces pervaded the entire universe, and stellar spirits influenced man ever so slightly. He honestly believed that a good doctor must have a basic understanding of the operation of celestial bodies. In spite of the fact that Agrippa played an important role in the drama of mental health, his name received no recognition until long beyond his death. Living in a *Zeitgeist* of tormented restlessness, he faced one obloquy after the other throughout his public career.

Much of his trouble began in 1518, when as advocate to the city of Metz, Agrippa clashed head on with the relentless Inquisitor Nicolas Savin. Henry Morley tells us that Agrippa defended a woman accused of witchcraft. The damning evidence against her was the fact that her mother had been burned as a witch! Hearing this kind of a twisted theory of heredity, Agrippa exploded and denounced Savin as, 'that brotherkin (I err), that great, swollen and fat brother, Nicolas Savin, of the Dominican Order. The hypocrite dissembles his iniquity under the shadow of the Gospel! . . .' Savin countered by a clever bit of legal chicanery to bring the girl to trial. Agrippa, seething by now, wrote the judge:[1]

'I have excepted against this man as impertinent, intrusive and incompetent to exercise in this case the judicial function; but lest you be led astray by false prophets who claim to be Christ, and are Antichrist, I pray your reverence to bear with a word of help, and only pay attention to a conversation lately held with me upon the position of this article by the before-named bloodthirsty brother. For he asserted superciliously that the fact was; in the highest degree decisive, and enough to warrant torture and not unreasonably he asserted it according to the knowledge of his sect, which he produced presently out of the depth of the *Malleus Maleficarum* and the principles of peripatetic Theology. . . . Oh, egregious sophism! Is it thus that in these days we theologise? Do fragments like these move us to the torturing of harmless women?'

Sure to retaliate, Savin had his revenge. Agrippa was driven out of Metz and spent his remaining years being hated, maligned and slandered. Like Paracelsus, he died alone, destitute and broken. No notary helped him, nor did anyone toss pennies to the poor at his funeral. During this miserable period, he had only his dog *Monsieur*, a black French poodle, and a bitch named *Mademoiselle*. The male dog warmed the master's cold feet, slept under his bed and ate at his table but rumour spread that Agrippa was a conjurer and his pet, a demon. In literature he was often assailed and ridiculed. Rabelais reviled him as Herr Trippa. Butler jested about the devil-dog in *Hudibras*. Written in mock-heroic couplets, the poem is replete with burlesque and travesty:

> Agrippa kept a Stygian pug,
> I' th' garb and habit of a dog,
> That was his tutor, and the cur
> Read to the occult philosopher,
> And taught him subt'ly to maintain
> All other sciences are vain.

Robert Southey also told a monkish tale about him. His ballad, appearing in Westbury (1798), concerned a young man who begged Agrippa's wife until she let him into the doctor's locked library.[2]

> On the Study-table, a book there lay,
> Which Agrippa himself had been reading that day;
> The letters were written with blood therein,
> And the leaves were made of dead men's skin;
>
> And these horrible leaves of magic between
> Were the ugliest pictures that ever were seen;
> The likeness of things so foul to behold,
> That what they were is not fit to be told.

The lad began to study the forbidden books. And as he read, he was torn to bits by the griffin claw of the devil. The moral of the story:

AGRIPPA TO BODIN

Henceforth let all young men take heed
How in a conjurer's books they read.

An explosive bundle of restless energy and dazzling paradoxes, Agrippa was one of the most unpredictable medical men
of his day. While in his middle twenties, he wrote *Three Books
of Occult Philosophy*, a work that was republished centuries
later.[3] Still, he lived to attack his own views vehemently in
De Vanitate Scientiarum, which exposed by 'an invective
declamation', the droll vanity of all esoteric practices. Taking
biographical data, one could analyse the contradictions and
inconsistencies of Agrippa in terms of the following antinomies:

> Upheld yet opposed occultism.
> Reckless yet conservative.
> Ambitious yet modest.
> Good soldier, yet hated war.
> Yearned to settle yet moved about.
> Often unemployed yet worked hard.
> Made friends yet had more enemies.
> Devoted husband yet thrice married.
> Brilliant scholar yet man of action.
> Loved the world yet fought it.
> Ever the same yet ever changing.
> Defeated yet victorious.

Not many escaped his burning words—words that scorched
theologians, philosophers and doctors alike. He had an astonishing knack for displacing aggression to others and what was even
more astonishing, he often got away with it. Take for instance,
the time that his ironic pen pierced the shield of arrogance and
pretext which his medical colleagues held so firmly:
'The greatest reputation is attained by those physicians who
are recommended by splendid costumes, many rings and jewels,
a distant fatherland, tedious travels, a strange religion especially
the Hindu and Mohammedan, and who combine with these a
monstrous shamelessness in the praising of their medicines and
cures. They observe times and hours most exactly, dispense
their medicines always according to the astrological calendar,

and hang all kinds of amulets on the patients. Simple and native medicines are quite neglected. Costly foreign remedies are preferred, which later are mixed in such enormous numbers that the action of one is counteracted by that of another, so that no human sagacity can foresee the effects which will arise from such an abominable mixture.'

Erasmus advised Agrippa to dilute the vitriol but Erasmus, himself, poured on the acid full strength when in *Praise of Folly* he described medicine: 'The whole Art as it is now practised is but one incorporated compound of craft and imposture.' If the twentieth century produced a disciple of Agrippa to challenge that small number of self-styled custodians of the mentally ill who do little more than 'commit 'em, shock 'em, drug 'em and forget 'em', would they, the custodians, then cry that no one should infringe upon their legally constituted rights? Any modern Agrippa may escape the charge of being a conjurer but would he escape the label of being 'an immature, hostile personality acting out infantile frustrations'? And if a rough iconoclast cannot avoid the mish-mash of barbaric terms that are sprinkled so liberally throughout the devil's lexicon of psychiatry, what can a helpless, inarticulate patient do?

A final impression, one gathers from a study of his biography, is that Agrippa went far very fast. In a relatively short career, he served as secretary to Maximilian, doctor of divinity at Dole and Pavia, syndic and advocate to the city of Metz, physician to the Duchess of Anjou (mother of King Francis) and Counsellor to Emperor Charles. Consequently, he gained much data about world affairs from diplomatic sources that he contacted daily and not from a canine which imprudent vulgarism regarded as a demon. However, Agrippa's greatest singular claim to imperishable fame may be found in the last three years of his life when he accepted a seventeen-year-old mild-mannered domestic and student named Johann Weyer whose mind instigated the first revolution in mental health! But before we turn to Weyer, let us consider Paracelsus, a colleague of Agrippa, and a 'rebel' with the same cause.

Johann Weyer

François Rabelais

AGRIPPA TO BODIN

Paracelsus, son of a physican and a nurse, was born in a peaceful village near Zürich. At times, he responded to Philippus Aureolus Paracelsus Theophrastus Bombastus von Hohenheim or various combinations thereof, but he grew up without the second and third names. Aureolus described his golden hair. Some writers claimed that he selected Paracelsus because he ranked himself above Celsus—the custodian of medicine in old Rome. Bombastus characterized his behaviour very nicely— aggressive, fulminating, grandiose and impetuous. The strange but colourful personality of Paracelsus, no doubt, inspired Robert Browning to immortalize him in an epic poem, and Arthur Schnitzler to do likewise in a play.

By his open defiance of tradition, he made many enemies who seemed to annoy him wherever he went. One of the most un-popular doctors of his day, Paracelsus began his teaching by publicly burning the works of Galen and Avicenna—ancient authorities who had been respected highly by the medical faculties for centuries. Meanwhile, he declared if God would not help him, he would advise and consult with the devil. Notwith-standing his sincerity, he obviously ran into difficulty with associates, for his manner and temperament were especially suited to offend them, and like Agrippa, hard-hitting and two-fisted, he tried to reform a quixotic world. Humanists to the core, both men loved the common, cheese-eating people and both doggedly fought the pompous, well-fed physicians of their time. Paracelsus also earned a place in *Hudibras*:

> Bumbastus kept a devil's bird
> Shut in the pommel of his sword,
> That taught him all the cunning pranks
> Of past and future mountebanks.

While opposing the prevailing demonological ideas regarding mental illness, Paracelsus offered no original constructive theories of his own, for he, too, was an assiduous student of alchemy and astrology and hardly could be expected to envision a day of tranquillizers, modern drugs and aeronomy, the science of the upper atmosphere. Considered by some as the father of pharmacology, he prescribed mercury for lues, introduced mineral baths, and used arsenic, lead, opium and such in treatment. He also spoke of the influence of psychogenic factors:[4]

'Imagination and faith can cause and remove diseases. Confidence in the virtue of amulets is the whole secret of their efficacy. It is from faith that imagination draws power. Anyone who believes in the secret resources of Nature receives from Nature according to his own faith; let the object of your faith be real or imaginary, you will in an equal degree obtain the same results.'

For Paracelsus, each illness had a specific cause and hence a specific remedy and, attempting to reform medical arts, he denied the Galenic dictum of humoral lability, and inveighed the practice of naming diseases after saints. But in his book, *The Invisible Diseases* (1531), Paracelsus suddenly forgot his knowledge of chemistry and clinical symptoms and wrote more like a mystical philosopher, confusing alchemy with theosophy, feeling with reasoning and speculating with testing: diseases came from God as punishment for sin, he claimed; and those who committed suicide were inspired by the devil.

Elsewhere, however, Paracelsus does an about face in *De Generatione Stultorum*, one of the early references which related goitre and cretinism. It includes a truly moving appeal for the understanding and humane treatment of retardates. Then too, he displayed unusual perspicacity by associating sexual conflicts to hysteria and by alluding to the unconscious bases of neuroses.

At the same time, oddly enough, his *De Lunatics* recommended confession to prevent madness and burning to prevent demonic involvement. For those who are possessed by the devil and do not respond to the prescribed treatment, Paracelsus said that their only hope for a cure could be found in Christ, prayer and fasting. Paracelsus' influence is evident in the works of Robert Fludd, English physician, who defended the occultistic practices of the Rosicrucians.

In a volume about witches, Paracelsus charged that they were responsible for thunderstorms, that they produced diseases by shooting foreign bodies under the victim's skin and that they caused congenital anomalies. He added that a witch was born as such and that she could be recognized by the infallible sign of a hooked nose, the abstinence from sexual intercourse (particularly a widow), or by a preference for coitus on Thursdays, Fridays and Saturdays—never on Sunday. Paracelsus closes this text with a laudable humane plea in favour of 'saving' rather than burning the witches.

Erwin H. Ackerknecht, Professor at the University of Zürich, described the inconsistent Paracelsus with these words:[5] 'As a campaigner against ancient dogmas, and an unprejudiced observer and chemist, he undoubtedly stood at the cradle of modern medicine and psychiatry. But as a medieval mystic and immensely self-contradictory confabulator, he was often forced to support opposing factions; and thus he caused a great deal of confusion.'

JOHANN WEYER

Johann Weyer was born in Grave on the Maas River. Some biographers identified him as Dutch, others as German. One thing certain, all recognized him as a courageous physician and an able psychiatrist who rejected the popular belief in demons without equivocation and who replaced theories of demonology with his own theories of psychoses which he defended with clinical and objective observations of patients.

In 1563, Weyer published an exposé of the folly of witchcraft. To him witches were unfortunate human beings who confessed to any crime when they lost their rational powers, and consequently it would be a horrible mistake to torture them. He denied that they ever rode a broom or that the devil transformed them, or anyone else, into animals (lycanthropy), a superstition that was accepted by such learned men as Pietro Pomponazzi and Jean Fernel. According to Weyer, all of this was a diabolical illusion, acted only in dreams or observed as symptoms of insanity.[6]

John Oldham, the Jesuit satirist, likewise sneered at the myth of airborne witches. And Butler bantered the idea that people metamorphosed into animals. Both may be found in *Hudibras*:

> As men in sleep, though motionless they lie,
> Fledg'd by a dream, believe they mount and fly;
> So witches some enchanted wand bestride,
> And think they through the airy regions ride.
>
> . . . . .
>
> Transform'd himself to the ugly shapes
> Of wolves, and bears, baboons, and apes.

Studying each case of witchcraft carefully, Weyer concluded that all of them contained either a question of illness or of rascality. Therefore, he regarded the judges as butchers for sentencing the miserable wretches to the stake. Since many of the accused were delusional young ladies or harmless senile old women, Weyer advocated treating them with compassion and empathy. Despite strong opposition, his book expounding these views had remarkable success and passed through several printings while he still lived.[7]

One clinical account of witchcraft described Weyer as the true founder of modern psychiatry.[8] The Rhinish reformer added many original ideas toward a humane and intelligent understanding of the mentally ill. Along with Agrippa and Paracelsus, Weyer fired the opening salvo of the first psychiatric revolution. Their combined efforts offered psychopathology an identity of its own by its gradual emancipation from theology. To them, man's behaviour was determined by his relationships to other men and not influenced by metaphysical forces; and with them, a dawn of a new age shone on the horizon; a small beam of light illumined the path—a path that continued to be long, tortuous and uphill all the way.

With Weyer, the objective study of mental disorders began, yet in making his courageous move, he jeopardized his reputation and his personal safety, just as other opponents of superstition faced torture and execution for their enlightened humanistic views. The cards of life were then heavily stacked against these early rebels who dared to challenge the wishes of the masses, the laws and the churches. Confronted by such overwhelming odds, it is easy to see why progress in mental health was painfully slow.

By way of contrast, advancement in the objective approach to physical health was enormous. Interest in this respect grew rapidly because the patient who suffered organic distress wanted and sought relief. Throughout the Continent, the march of science was on: Ulrich von Hutten, poet-humanist, exposed syphilis; Andreas Vesalius reorganized the study of anatomy so completely that it gave the *coup de grâce* to Galenic medicine; Ambrose Paré made noteworthy strides in surgery; Hieronymus Aquapendente, the master of Harvey, wrote valuable papers on embryology; William Harvey traced the circulation of the blood. His *Essay on the Motion of the Heart and the Blood* appeared in 1628, and faced futile resistance. A physician friend, George Ent, supported it. John Dryden then quipped:

> From dark Oblivion Harvey's name shall save;
> While Ent keeps all the honour that he gave.

Harvey's discovery was a tremendous boon for physiology, but for the mentally ill, it meant more bloodletting. Some doctors even naïvely suggested transfusions to treat the insane. And so it went, right down the line—glorious success in physical health, but bitter frustration in mental health.

Relegating demonology to the domain of disordered minds and bizarre dreams did not, however, remove Weyer entirely from the shadows of black magic, because there were times when he reversed himself and ascribed strange powers to the devil and his attendants. In these cases, Weyer tried to convince others that the legendary Johann Faust, whom he called *magus*, was a sorcerer who had signed in blood a deal with the Evil one. The following illustration revealed Weyer's precarious position:[9]

'One of the best-known symptoms of bewitchment was the vomitting of bones, nails, needles, balls of wool, bunches of hair, and other things, some of which were so large that they could not have passed through the throat by any natural means. Such phenomena, Wier (Weyer) tells us, he had himself seen. How were they to be explained? Easily, according to Wier's general theory. Such articles, he says, are put into the patient's mouth by the devil, one after another, as fast as they come out. We cannot see him do this, either because he acts so rapidly that his motions are invisible, or because he fascinates our sight, or because he darkens our eyes, perhaps by interposing between them and the patient some aerial body.'

Today it is not rare to see signs in advanced psychotics that Weyer may have misunderstood and blamed on the devil. For example, those patients who reach the fourth or terminal stage of the schizophrenic sequence often fail to recognize edibles and have been known to grasp and ingest all sorts of objects which later were found in their stomachs or intestines.[10] A typical case revealed that a patient had died of an acute intestinal disorder and an autopsy discovered fourteen spoon handles in the colon, two spoon handles and a suspender clasp in the stomach and a rolled piece of shirt collar in the terminal ileum to cause the obstruction. This collection was regarded as relatively modest when compared with others which located balls of hair, pieces of metal, lumps of paper, chips of wood and various foreign items.

The forceful features of the post-Renaissance were not restricted to the works of Agrippa, Paracelsus and Weyer alone, for other aspects of writing had similar structural and tonal characteristics. Each and every branch developed and all in their way left a mark on mental health; François Rabelais in fiction, Jean Fernel in medicine and Jean Bodin in law. The pens that these men stroked and those who immediately followed them reflected the rhythm, the ebb and the flow of their culture while the world was being readied for a whole new concept of life.

FRANÇOIS RABELAIS

François Rabelais was a man of three professions—priest, doctor and teacher—who cherished the Greek ideals of integrating the whole person. Though he authored several medical papers and translated aphorisms of Hippocrates into Latin, Rabelais is best remembered for the grotesque and humorous novels, *Pantagruel* and *Gargantua*. In the latter, he had this to say regarding mental therapy:

'When Ponocrates knew Gargantua's vicious manner of living, he resolved to bring him up in another kind; but for a while he bore with him, considering that nature cannot endure such a change, without great violence. Therefore to begin his work the better, he requested a learned physician of that time, called Master Theodorus, seriously to perpend, if it were possible, how to bring Gargantua unto a better course. The said physician purged him canonically with Anticyrian-hellebore, by which medicine he cleansed all the alteration, and perverse habitude of his brain.'

Living in a time of bitter political and religious conflict, Rabelais safely introjected his unconventional ideas, covering them with a cloak of gaiety and irony, and in this manner tried to show what effect the stagnant medieval society had on mental health and personality development. The first edition of *Pantagruel* appeared under the pseudonym of Alcofribas Nasier, an anagram of his full name. To have written his racy mirth any other way would surely have been dangerous for him.

A careful analysis of his masterpieces reveals several antinomies about his own mental status. They give a profile of popular lore and yet of immense learning; of obscene buffoonery and yet of serious philosophy; of esoteric allegory and yet of crass realism; of uninhibited fantasy and yet of reliable reflection; of destructive satire and yet of constructive argument. And Rabelais, with all of his contradictions, still provided a clear panorama of the customs and interests of that time. Because of his enlightened humanism and steadfast opposition to the abuse of the mentally ill, one may assign him the epithet of a French Erasmus. With a trenchant pen, Rabelais acted out his protest, rejected charlatanesque forms of treatment, medical superstitions and obsolescent teaching methods.

Once that grandiose bug nipped Rabelais, it constricted the muscles around his ego like tetanus, and avoiding any contemporary counsellors, he attacked the monasteries, debunked legal methods and even argued (illogically of course) that women were no good. To him a woman should accept her biological destiny and not compete with a man. Did he happen to read *Urbain le Courtois*? 'If you wish to marry a wife, dear son, consider your own good; take none for her beauty nor any that have book learning, for they are often deceitful.'

The professional personality of Rabelais illustrated a true psychosynthesis. The monk who became a doctor and a teacher was no longer isolated from the main stream of human activities. Before Rabelais, the monk specialized in the study of the soul, for him to openly consider the body and mind of man was tantamount to heterodoxy. After Rabelais, these subterranean streams of thought slowly rose to the surface, until the clerics, craftsmen and academicians pooled together the divergent currents to create a wondrous lake for modern science. Eugene Field perpetuated the memory of the man who did so much here:

> Deny who may that Rabelais
> Is first in wit and learning,
> And yet all smile and marvel while
> His brilliant leaves they're turning.

THE WITCHMONGERS

Jean Fernel was a professor in Paris who supposedly believed that the devil could transform humans into animals. This did not, however, prevent him from contributing to medicine in general and mental health in particular. His topographic concept of disease, evolved from an analytic (Cnidian) framework, preceded the symptomologic viewpoint of Felix Plater, a theory in which he compared anatomy to medicine as geography is to history. The fact that Fernel corrected several Galenic dictums in itself made his plan valid. On the one hand, he fostered the organic theories of hysteria as being due to a migrating uterus, of melancholia as related to the spleen, of hypochondriasis as beginning below the costal arch and of phrenitis as localized in the diaphragm. On the other, he recognized the luetic origin of some aneurysms.[11]

Sensitive to psychologic factors, Fernel built a fortune practising medicine after he overcame the sterility of Catherine de Medici and restored the health of Diane de Potiers. Once he tried to evade the dubious responsibility of royal physician by feigning pleurisy, only to have the ruse fail since Henry II drafted him as his personal doctor in the campaigns to retake Calais. Considered to be a man of saturnine nature, Fernel possessed a deep, sincere concern for all of his patients. This depressive trait worked against him and he died griefstricken soon after the loss of his wife.[12]

Jean Bodin, a native of Anvers, probably of Jewish ancestry, rose from an obscure beginning to become a widely known French publicist and political economist. He earned a law degree at Toulouse, lectured on jurisprudence there, practised in Paris. But failing as a trial lawyer, Bodin turned to literary pursuits. Unlike earlier jurisconsults who drew from Greek and Roman antiquity, he took from the leading European countries of his day for references, meticulously gathered concrete data, tiny details of daily living and current events to formulate in a semi-objective way laws of political science. Therefore, it surprised his biographers, no end, when this seemingly scientific man changed his thinking and published *De la Démonomanie des Sorciers* to prove the existence of sorcerers. Herein, he argued for the legality of their condemnation, on the basis of 'experience' and respect for *res judicatae* or the reliability of the courts. Such a belief in witchcraft applied the same reasoning as his principles of government.[13]

Keen of intellect and logic-chopping with determination, Bodin became a bookish witchmonger who hammered away at Johann Weyer's enlightened view with a vengeance. In a frontal attack upon the father of psychiatry, he used sixty-five pages to refute the opinion of Weyer and to differentiate legal and medical insanity. The tradition that the French legist established remains a source of confusion today, for a patient may be still judged 'legally sane' and 'clinically insane' at the same time. When Bodin heard that Weyer had written another book, he held up the publication of his own and added a long chapter in a futile attempt to prevent witch-hunting of the sixteenth century from fading into obscurity.

Bodin believed that only 'a very ignorant or a wicked man' could have written *De Praestigiis* and *De Lamiis*. And since Weyer was not ignorant, Bodin concluded that he must be wicked, a 'protector of witches'. 'I cannot read all this without horror,' he cried. Bodin admitted that Weyer quoted the Bible, but only to misrepresent it. His effort to create a self-image of piety was merely a fraud, for if 'he sometimes spoke of God and the Law, it is an old imposture that has always been used by Satan and his legions'. Weyer happens to be one of them, for was he not the pupil of Cornelius Agrippa, 'his master Sorcerer, the greatest sorcerer of the age'? Has not Weyer himself said that he led Agrippa's dog on a leash—that black dog—that devil dog? Because Agrippa wrote a book which disproved his own *Occult Philosophy* meant nothing to Bodin who charged that the devil often adorns himself with a halo to disguise his true wickedness.

The Frenchman also rationalized in various other ways when he accused Weyer. Among Bodin's most poignant arguments of refutation was the one that referred to Weyer's feminism: 'God's law wanted to prove that men are less corrupted with the affliction (witchcraft) than women'. There were fifty witches to one sorcerer. Quintilian believed that women were worse than men. Plato even said that woman was a transitional stage from wild beast to man. Women were liars. Women had larger intestines than men—wisdom never came from women. How dare Weyer assert that witches were melancholic women? As a physician he should know that men could become melancholic but not women. Women were by nature 'cold and humid' and they never suffered from gout; melancholy came from heat and dryness. How could women develop that disease of men? Bodin was disgusted with the 'fanatical errors of those who wanted to defend women as melancholics'.

In 1950, Bodin became Attorney-General at Laon. Regarded as a champion of conscience and religious tolerance, he sided with the *ligue*, and persuaded many to do likewise. Never openly abandoning the Catholic faith, he died of the plague at the age of sixty-six, and was interred at a Franciscan cemetery. Bodin left a manuscript titled *Colloquium Heptaplomers*, a paper on spiritualism and, like his other superstitious writings, displayed anti-Christian subtleties and definite hostility towards Catholicism. Hence, in 1629, all his works were placed on the *Index*, and in 1900 the prohibition was continued on his *Universae Naturae Theatrum*: 'To judge by his writings,' said François Toussaint, 'he was a bizarre, inconstant and superficial man'.

BIBLIOGRAPHY

1. Henry Morley, *The Life of Henry Cornelius Agrippa von Nettesheim*, Chapman and Hall, London, 1856, 2, pp. 57-63.
2. Robert Southey, *Poetical Works*, Crowell, New York, 1837, p. 431.
3. Heinrich C. Agrippa, *Three Books of Occult Philosophy*, Hahn & Whitehead, Chicago, 1898.
4. James J. Walsh, *Psychotherapy*, Appleton, New York, 1913, p. 15.
5. Sulammith Wolff, Translator, *A Short History of Psychiatry*, Hafner, London, 1959, p. 25.
6. Johann Weyer, *De Praestigiis Daemonum*, Oporinum, Basilieae, 1563.
7. Carl Binz, *Doktor Johann Weyer*, Marcus, Bonn, 1885.
8. Gregory Zilboorg, *The Medical Man and the Witch During the Renaissance*, Johns Hopkins, Baltimore, 1935.
9. George L. Kittredge, *Witchcraft in Old and New England*, Harvard University, Cambridge, 1929, p. 339.
10. Silvano Arieti, *Interpretation of Schizophrenia*, Brunner, New York, 1955, p. 364.

11. Ilza Veith, ' Psychiatric Nosology: From Hippocrates to Krae-pelin', *American Journal of Psychiatry*, 114 : 5, 1957, pp. 385-391.
12. Fielding H. Garrison, *History of Medicine*, Saunders, Phila-delphia, 1929, p. 196.
13. Jean Bodin, *De la Démonomanie des Sorciers*, Coninx, Anvers 1593.

INDEX OF NAMES

INDEX OF NAMES

INDEX OF NAMES

INDEX OF SUBJECTS

INDEX OF SUBJECTS